THE
COLLECTOR'S
LIBRARY
EVERLASTING
DIARY

THE
COLLECTOR'S
LIBRARY
EVERLASTING
DIARY

Compiled by
ROSEMARY GRAY

Collector's Library

This diary published in 2013 by

Collector's Library

to celebrate the tenth anniversary
of CRW Publishing Limited
69 Gloucester Crescent, London NW1 7EG
www.collectors-library.com

ISBN 978 1 907360 96 1

Compiled by Rosemary Gray

Typeset in Great Britain by Antony Gray
Printed and bound in China by Imago

THE
COLLECTOR'S
LIBRARY
EVERLASTING
DIARY

Illustration from *Peter Pan*

January 1st

1879 – E. M. Forster was born in London. Although registered Henry Morgan Forster he was accidentally named Edward Morgan at his christening – so to distinguish him from his father he was always called Morgan. Katharine Mansfield wryly observed in 1917: 'E. M. Forster never gets any further than warming the teapot. He's a rare hand at that. Feel this teapot. Is it not beautifully warm? Yes, but there ain't going to be no tea.' How wrong she was! His masterpiece, *A Passage to India*, was published in 1924.

'Give me life, with its struggles and victories, with its failures and hatreds, with its deep moral meaning and its unknown goal!'

'The Other Side of the Hedge' from *The Machine Stops and Other Stories*

January 2nd

1842 – Mary Ann Evans (who later wrote as George Eliot) failed to attend church as usual; she had 'lost her faith in Church doctrine'. Because this caused her father such distress, she agreed to continue to attend church with him but reserved the right to think her own thoughts during the service.

———

He said he should prefer not to know the sources of the Nile, and that there should be some unknown regions preserved as hunting-grounds for the poetic imagination.

Middlemarch

January 3rd

1841 – Herman Melville sailed from Fairhaven, Massachusetts, on the whaler *Acushnet* bound for the Pacific Ocean. He was twenty-two but considered that his 'life began that day'.

———

A whaleship was my Yale College and my Harvard.

Moby Dick

January 4th

1929 – Virginia Woolf wrote in her diary: 'Still talking about Lawrence, a very very good writer but his last book DISGUSTING.' D. H. Lawrence's *Lady Chatterley's Lover* had been published in Florence in the summer of 1928.

———

'John Thomas says good-night to Lady Jane, a little droopingly, but with a hopeful heart.'

Lady Chatterley's Lover

January 5th

1821 – Lord Byron ordered 'pistols and greatcoat, as usual' when 'going out to make love'. He was living in Pisa at the time, near to his friends Percy Bysshe and Mary Shelley who were renting a house on the Italian coast.

———

'We will each write a ghost story,' said Lord Byron ...
   I busied myself *to think of a story* – a story ... which would speak to the mysterious fears of our nature,

and awaken thrilling horror – one to make the reader
dread to look round, to curdle the blood and quicken
the beatings of the heart.

MARY SHELLEY's Introduction to *Frankenstein*

January 6th

1883 – Kahlil Gibran was born into a Maronite
Catholic family in northern Lebanon. He is the third
best-selling poet of all time, behind Shakespeare and
Lao-Tzu.

———

Work is love made visible. And if you cannot work
with love but only with distaste, it is better that you
should leave your work and sit at the gate of the
temple and take alms of those who work with joy.

The Prophet

January 7th

1925 – Gerald Durrell was born in India and as an infant spent most of his time with his ayah, who memorably took him to the zoo for the first time. Living with his family in Corfu in the 1930s his interest in animals and the living world developed and grew into a lifelong passion.

―――――――

His warning came too late, for I had already placed my hand on the bird's back and was gently running my fingers over the silken feathering. The gull crouched, opened his beak slightly, and the dark iris of his eye contracted with surprise, but he was so taken aback by my audacity that he did nothing.

My Family and Other Animals

January 8th

1824 – Wilkie Collins was born in Marylebone. His father and his godfather, David Wilkie, were both well-known painters. He was bullied at school by a boy who would force Collins to tell him a story before allowing him to go to sleep. 'It was this brute who awakened in me, his poor little victim, a power of which but for him I might never have been aware.'

―――――――

There, in the middle of the broad, bright high-road –
there, as if it had that moment sprung out of the earth
or dropped from the heaven – stood the figure of a
solitary woman, dressed from head to foot in white
garments, her face bent in grave inquiry on mine, her
hand pointing to the dark cloud over London.

The Woman in White

January 9th

1923 – Death of Katherine Mansfield, whose writing,
Virginia Woolf confessed, was 'the only writing I have
ever been jealous of'.

———

'What enemy do we now perceive advancing against
us, you whom I ride now, as we stand pawing this
stretch of pavement? It is death.'

VIRGINIA WOOLF, *The Waves*

January 10th

1961 – Dashiell Hammett, 'the dean of the "hard-boiled" school of detective fiction', died in New York. Towards the end 'the phonograph was unplayed, the typewriter was untouched, the beloved foolish gadgets unopened in their packages'. As a veteran of both World Wars, he was buried at Arlington National Cemetery.

The day of his death came on 10 January 1961. I will never write that biography because I cannot write about my closest, my most beloved friend.

He did not wish to die and I like to think he didn't know he was dying. But I keep from myself even now the possible meaning of a night, very late, a short time before his death. I came into his room and for the only time in the years I knew him there were tears in his eyes and the book was lying unread.

LILLIAN HELLMAN

January 11th

1928 – Just after 9 p.m. Thomas Hardy died. His heart is buried in the graveyard of his native parish, but his ashes are in Poets' Corner in Westminster Abbey.

It is hard for a woman to define her feelings in language which is chiefly made by men to express theirs.

Far from the Madding Crowd

January 12th

1836 – The *Beagle* carrying Charles Darwin docked in Sydney Harbour towards the end of his epic voyage. He wrote that his findings during the expedition 'seemed to throw some light on the origin of species'. His sensational and controversial work on evolution was published on 24 November 1859.

We will now discuss in a little more detail the Struggle for Existence.

On the Origin of Species

---

1. Geospiza magnirostris   2. Geospiza fortis
3. Geospiza parvula   4. Certhidea olivacea

January 13th

1941 – Having fled Paris following the Nazi occupation of France, James Joyce died in Zurich. The author of *Ulysses*, he is considered to be one of the most influential writers in the modernist avant-garde of the twentieth century.

———

His soul swooned slowly as he heard the snow falling faintly through the universe and faintly falling, like the descent of their last end, upon all the living and the dead.

'The Dead' from *Dubliners*

January 14th

1898 – Lewis Carroll died at his sister's home in Guildford of pneumonia following influenza and is buried there in the Mount Cemetery. At the time of his death, *Alice in Wonderland* had become the most popular children's book in England and by 1932 it was one of the most popular in the world.

———

And if I have written anything to add to those stores of innocent and healthy amusement that are laid up in books for the children I love so well, it is surely something I may hope to look back upon without shame and sorrow (as how much of life must then be recalled!) when my turn comes to walk through the valley of shadows.

‘An Easter Greeting’ from *Through the Looking-Glass*

January 15th

1928 – The casket containing the heart of Thomas Hardy was laid on the altar steps of Stinsford Parish Church, the church he had attended with his family as a child and the church where the ashes of both his wives, Emma and Florence, are interred.

––––––

With a cup of tea in his hand, [Hardy] made jokes about bishops at the Athenaeum Club ... Apparently, he considered bishops fair game, but soon began censuring Sir Edmund Gosse, who had recently stayed with them, for a breach of good taste in imitating his old friend Henry James's way of drinking soup. Loyalty to his friends was always a passion with Hardy.

ROBERT GRAVES, *Goodbye to All That*

January 16th

1794 – Edward Gibbon, the 'English giant of the Enlightenment', died from peritonitis following three operations to relieve acute scrotal swelling.

––––––

Corruption, the most infallible symptom of constitutional liberty.

The Decline and Fall of the Roman Empire

January 17th

1820 – Anne Brontë, the youngest of the Brontë children, was born in Thornton shortly before the family moved to Haworth Parsonage. Anne wrote perhaps the most shocking of the Brontës' novels. Her depiction of alcoholism and debauchery was profoundly disturbing for nineteenth-century sensibilities. The slamming of the heroine's bedroom door against her husband reverberated throughout Victorian England.

───────

I hate him – I hate him! – But God have mercy on his miserable soul! – and make him see and feel his guilt – I ask no other vengeance! If he could but fully know and truly feel my wrongs, I should be well avenged; and I could freely pardon all; but he is so lost, so hardened in his heartless depravity that, in this life, I believe he never will.

The Tenant of Wildfell Hall

January 18th

1936 – Rudyard Kipling died. To a magazine that had prematurely announced his death, he had written, 'I've just read that I am dead. Don't forget to delete me from your list of subscribers.' Henry James had said of him: 'Kipling strikes me as the most complete man of genius that I have ever known.'

───────

Kim sat up and smiled. The terrible weakness had dropped from him like an old shoe. His tongue itched for free speech again, and but a week back the lightest word clogged it like ashes. The pain in his neck (he must have caught it from the lama) had gone with the heavy dengue-aches and the evil taste in the mouth. The two old women, a little, but not much, more careful about their veils now, clucked as merrily as the hens that had entered pecking through the open door.

Kim

January 19th

1809 – Edgar Poe was born was born in Boston to parents in the acting profession. When his father abandoned the family and his mother died he was fostered by a wealthy merchant, John Allan, and became Edgar Allan Poe. His life was to be fraught with drama and tragedy.

———

The corpse, already greatly decayed and clotted with gore, stood erect before the eyes of the spectators. Upon its head, with red extended mouth and solitary eye of fire, sat the hideous beast whose craft had seduced me into murder, and whose informing voice had consigned me to the hangman. I had walled the monster up within the tomb!

'The Black Cat' from *Tales of Mystery and Imagination*

January 20th

1893 – Lord Alfred Douglas sent Oscar Wilde a sonnet he had written, 'Old Sarum Close'. Oscar's extravagant reply fell into the wrong hands due to Bosie's carelessness, thus beginning the train of events culminating in Wilde's prosecution for gross indecency.

———

Wilde was advised to go abroad to avoid the trial – his reply: 'Everyone wants me to go abroad. One can't keep going abroad unless one is a missionary, or, what comes to the same thing, a commercial traveller.'

January 21st

1920 – Katherine Mansfield wrote from Menton: 'If I don't get well here, I'll never get well.' Defeated by her tuberculosis, she suffered a fatal pulmonary haemorrhage three years later, after running up a flight of stairs to show her husband, J. Middleton Murry, how well she was. She was thirty-four.

Last night I read *The Well-Beloved* by Thomas Hardy. It really is *appallingly bad, simply rotten* – withered, bony and pretentious. This is very distressing. I thought it was going to be such a find and hugged it home from the library as though I were a girl of fifteen ... You won't like me writing this about him. But don't you know the feeling? If a man is 'wonderful' you want to fling up your arms and cry, 'Oh, do *go on* being wonderful. Don't be less wonderful. (Which is unreasonable, of course.)

Letter to John Middleton Murry

January 22nd

1903 – *The Wizard of Oz*, a musical extravaganza based on the children's fantasy written in 1900 by Frank L. Baum, premièred on Broadway.

UNT EM had just come out of the house to water the cabbages when she looked up and saw Dorothy running towards her.

'My darling child!' she cried, folding the little girl in her arms and covering her face with kisses; 'where in the world did you come from?'

'From the land of Oz,' said Dorothy, gravely. 'And here is Toto, too. And oh, Aunt Em, I'm so glad to be at home again!'

The Wizard of Oz

January 23rd

1789 – John Cleland died in London. James Boswell described him as that 'fine sly malcontent' and reported how he had found him living alone, shunned by all, with an ancient and ugly woman as his sole servant.

————

Ungracious then as the task may be, I shall recall to view those scandalous stages of my life out of which I emerg'd, at length, to the enjoyment of every blessing in the power of love, health and fortune to bestow.

Fanny Hill

January 24th

1862 – Edith Wharton was born into the wealthy family of George Frederic Jones in New York City and was given the sort of privileged upbringing few other families could afford for their children (hence the expression 'Keeping up with the Joneses'). Her novels and stories are written with a brilliant natural wit and acute social and psychological insight.

————

As her mother had been a Rushworth, and her last unhappy marriage had linked her to one of the crazy Chiverses, New York looked indulgently on her eccentricities; but when she returned with her little orphaned niece, whose parents had been popular in spite of their regrettable taste for travel, people thought it a pity that the pretty child should be in such hands.

The Age of Innocence

January 25th

1874 – Somerset Maugham was born in the British Embassy in Paris – technically on British soil. This was a wise precaution on the part of his father as children born on French soil could in later life be conscripted for military service (France was recovering from the recent Franco-Prussian War).

At last she stopped, panting. Her face was no longer human, it was distorted with cruelty and rage and pain. You would never have thought that this quiet, refined woman was capable of such a fiendish passion. Mr Joyce took a step backwards. He was absolutely aghast at the sight of her. It was not a face, it was a gibbering, hideous mask.

'The Letter' from
Best Short Stories of Somerset Maugham

January 26th

1920 – Virginia Woolf wrote in her diary: 'The day after my birthday; in fact I'm thirty-six. Well, I've no doubt I'm a great deal happier than I was at twenty-eight; & happier today than I was yesterday having this afternoon arrived at some idea of a new form for a new novel.'

———

Odd, incredible; she had never been so happy. Nothing could be slow enough; nothing last too long. No pleasure could equal, she thought, straightening the chairs, pushing in one book on the shelf, this having done with the triumphs of youth, lost herself in the process of living, to find it, with a shock of delight, as the sun rose, as the day sank.

Mrs Dalloway

January 27th

1832 – Charles Lutwidge Dodgson, later known by his pen name Lewis Carroll, was born into a fast-growing family in a small Cheshire parsonage.

———

'Cheshire Puss,' she began, rather timidly, as she did not at all know whether it would like the name: however, it only grinned a little wider. 'Come, it's pleased so far,' thought Alice, and she went on. 'Would you tell me, please, which way I ought to go from here?'

'That depends a good deal on where you want to get to,' said the Cat.

'I don't much care where – ' said Alice.

'Then it doesn't matter which way you go,' said the Cat.

' – so long as I get *somewhere*,' Alice added as an explanation.

Alice's Adventures in Wonderland

January 28th

1939 – W. B. Yeats died in Menton and was buried after a quiet family funeral. He left the instruction: 'In a year's time when the newspapers have forgotten me, dig me up and plant me in Sligo.' His remains were reinterred there in 1948; his epitaph is taken from 'Under Ben Bulben':

> Cast a cold eye
> On Life and Death.
> Horseman, pass by!

Collected Poems of W. B. Yeats

January 29th

1845 – One of the most famous poems ever written, 'The Raven' by Edgar Allan Poe was published in the *New York Evening Mirror* and made Poe widely popular. The poem was partly inspired by the talking raven in *Barnaby Rudge* by Charles Dickens.

> Take thy beak from out my heart, and take
>   thy form from off my door!
>   Quoth the Raven, 'Nevermore.'

from Tales and Poems of Edgar Allan Poe

January 30th

1995 – Gerald Durrell died of septicaemia shortly after a liver transplant. His ashes are buried in Jersey Zoo.

———

The coffin was standing upright, looking like a silver chrysalis, and at its lower end a portion had been removed so that the saint's feet ... peeped out. As each person reached the coffin he bent, kissed the feet, and murmured a prayer, while at the top of the sarcophagus the saint's black and withered face peered out of a glass panel with an expression of acute distaste.

My Family and Other Animals

January 31st

1879 – Joseph Conrad arrived in Sydney Harbour via the Cape of Good Hope on the clipper ship *Duke of Sunderland*; the long voyage had been his first genuine service at sea.

———

But for me all the East is contained in that vision of my youth. It is all in that moment when I opened my young eyes on it. I came upon it from a tussle with the sea – and I was young – and I saw it looking at me.

'Youth' from *Heart of Darkness and Other Stories*

February 1st

1918 – Muriel Spark was born in Edinburgh and educated at James Gillespie's High School for Girls, the model for the Marcia Blaine School.

———

'This is Stanley Baldwin who got in as Prime Minister and got out again ere long,' said Miss Brodie. 'Miss Mackay retains him on the wall because she believes in the slogan "Safety First". But Safety does not come first. Goodness, Truth and Beauty come first. Follow me.'

The Prime of Miss Brodie

February 2nd

1918 – With 'aeroplanes droning invisible', Virginia and Leonard Woolf spent 'our usual evening, alone happily, knee deep in papers', at their home in Richmond. Days before, 'the guns were so near that I didn't like to fetch a pair of shoes left in the bedroom'.

———

How tired I am ... of phrases that come down beautifully with all their feet on the ground!

The Waves

February 3rd

1924 – Virginia Woolf met Arnold Bennett and found him 'a lovable sealion, with chocolate eyes, drooping lids, & a protruding tusk'.

———

The lawn was the world; they were up here together, on this exalted station, she thought, looking at old Mr Carmichael, who seemed (though they had not said a word all this time) to share her thoughts. And she would never see him again perhaps. He was growing old. Also, she remembered, smiling at the slipper that dangled from his foot, he was growing famous. People said that his poetry was 'so beautiful'. They went and published things he had written forty years ago.

To the Lighthouse

February 4th

1915 – Mary Braddon died in Richmond. Intellectually ahead of her time, she had been a prolific writer, and her most famous novel, *Lady Audley's Secret*, has been in print ever since its publication in 1862.

———

She had hanged herself deliberately about an hour before Daniel found her, in the early grey of morning. The doctor, who was summoned from Holcroft, was able to declare the time at which she had slain herself, but there was no one who could say what sudden access of terror had impelled her to the desperate act, or under what slow torture of nervous apprehension her mind had given way.

'The Shadow in the Corner' from *Best Ghost Stories*

February 5th

1878 – *Punch* magazine in its obituary for George Cruikshank, famous as an illustrator of Dickens and of many other authors, described him as a man whose 'nature had something childlike in its transparency'. Upon his death it was discovered that during two marriages he had fathered eleven illegitimate children with a mistress who had been a former servant.

———

Child as he was, he was desperate with hunger, and reckless with misery. He rose from the table; and advancing to the master, basin and spoon in hand, said, somewhat alarmed at his own temerity: 'Please, sir, I want some more.'

The master was a fat, healthy man; but he turned

very pale. He gazed in stupefied astonishment on the small rebel for some seconds, and then clung for support to the copper. The assistants were paralysed with wonder; the boys with fear.

CHARLES DICKENS, *Oliver Twist*

George Cruikshank

February 6th

1907 – On the eve of her sister Vanessa's marriage to Clive Bell, Virginia Woolf promised 'to abide well content always adoring you now as before', although she confessed to Violet Dickinson: 'When I ... see that funny little creature twitching his pink skin and jerking out his little spasms of laughter I wonder what odd freak there is in Nessa's eyesight.'

———

There can be no doubt, I thought, pushing aside the newspaper, that our mean lives, unsightly as they are, put on splendour and have meaning only under the eyes of love.

The Waves

February 7th

1812 – Charles Dickens was born in Portsmouth. His earliest years seem to have been idyllic, though he thought himself 'a very small and not-particularly-taken-care-of boy'.

———

Whether I shall turn out to be the hero of my own life, or whether that station will be held by anybody else, these pages must show. To begin my life with the beginning of my life, I record that I was born (as I have been informed and believe) on a Friday, at twelve o'clock at night. It was remarked that the clock began to strike, and I began to cry, simultaneously.

David Copperfield

February 8th

1924 – E. M. Forster told Virginia Woolf that she had 'got further into the soul [in *Jacob's Room*] than any other novelist'. His maxim was, 'Only connect! ... Only connect the prose and the passion, and both will be exalted, and human love will be seen at its height.'

———

He cared for the universe, for the tiny tangle in it that we call civilisation, for his fellow men who had made the tangle and who transcended it. Love, the love of humanity, warmed him; and even when he was thinking of other matters, was looking at Orion perhaps in the cold winter evenings, a pang of joy, too sweet for description, would thrill him, and he would feel sure that our highest impulses have some eternal value, and will be completed hereafter. So full a nature could not brood over death.

'The Point of It' from
The Machine Stops and Other Stories

February 9th

1881 – Dostoevsky died in St Petersburg at the age of fifty-nine. 'He looked as though he were asleep, gently smiling as though he could see something beautiful.'

———

And if at that moment he had been capable of seeing and reasoning more correctly, if he had been able to realise all the difficulties of his position, the hopelessness, the hideousness and the absurdity of it, if he could have understood how many obstacles and, perhaps, crimes he had still to overcome or to commit ... it is very possible that he would have flung up everything, and would have gone to give himself up, and not from fear, but from simple horror and loathing of what he had done.

Crime and Punishment

February 10th

1932 – Edgar Wallace died in Beverly Hills. Flags in Fleet Street flew at half-mast and the bells of St Bride's tolled in mourning.

———

His methods were unique: nobody but Len would have taken a furnished house in Burford Square and staged an elaborate murder mystery in order to bring all the police in the neighbourhood running to that one particular spot and leave unguarded the place he wished to burgle.

'The Mind-Reader' from *Vintage Detective Stories*

February 11th

1940 – John Buchan died in office as the Governor General of Canada after suffering a stroke and falling from his horse.

———

His brow retreated and the stubbly back of his neck ran forward to meet it ... His head was exactly the shape of a pear with the sharp end topmost ... Here was the German of caricature, the real German, the fellow we were up against. He was as hideous as a hippopotamus, but effective.

Greenmantle

February 12th

1945 – E. M. Forster dined with Harold Nicolson at the Travellers Club.

———

Morgan is easily drowned ... He is an unworldly, transparent character, whimsical & detached ... & very sensitive; an attractive character to me, though from his very qualities it takes as long to know him as it used to take to put one's gallipot over a humming bird moth. More truly, he resembles a vaguely rambling butterfly, since there is no intensity or rapidity about him. To dominate the talk would be odious to him.

VIRGINIA WOOLF

February 13th

1887 – In *The Athenaeum*'s obituary for Mrs Henry Wood, her pen was said to have been active 'up to the last'. Leo Tolstoy wrote to his brother on 9 March 1892 that he was 'reading Mrs Henry Wood's wonderful novel *Within the Maze*'.

———

It is an awful blight upon a man when he is innocent, one that he may never quite live down. Suspicions must arise, I know that, of the innocent as well as the guilty, and they must undergo preliminary examinations in public and submit to legal enquiries; but time enough to proclaim who the man is when evidence strengthens against him, and he is committed for trial; until then let his name be suppressed. At least that is my opinion.'

'The Ebony Box' from *Vintage Detective Stories*

February 14th

1927 – Arnold Bennett wrote: 'Aldous Huxley is getting more into the habit of using such words as inconceivable, incredible, fantastic. These three are his favourite words, and one of them comes into nearly every sentence. His general knowledge is extraordinarily good. It is inconceivable, incredible and fantastic.'

We had tea at the 17 Club. One room was crowded, & silent; at the end of the other Aldous Huxley & a young woman in grey velvet held what should have been a private conversation. A. has a deliberate & rather dandified way of speaking. All we learned & virtuous people bent over our reforming papers in dead silence; an occasional sentence of the muffled dialogue came out plain from the end of the room now & then.

VIRGINIA WOOLF

February 15th

1919 – Wilfred Owen was awarded the Military Cross for 'conspicuous gallantry', posthumously. He was killed on 4 November 1918, days before the Armistice.

———

What passing-bells for these who die as cattle?
  Only the monstrous anger of the guns.
  Only the stuttering rifles' rapid rattle
Can patter out their hasty orisons.
No mockeries for them from prayers or bells,
  Nor any voice of mourning save the choirs –
The shrill, demented choirs of wailing shells;
  And bugles calling for them from sad shires ...

'Anthem for Doomed Youth' from
Poetry of the First World War

February 16th

2012 – Frederick Forsyth was awarded the Cartier Diamond Dagger by the Crime Writers' Association.

———

He could see the features quite clearly, the brow shaded by the peak of the *képi*, the peering eyes, the prow-like nose. He saw the raised saluting hand come down from the peak of the cap, the crossed wires of the sight were spot on the exposed temple ...

The Day of the Jackal

Illustration from *Cider with Rosie*

February 17th

1922 – Virginia Woolf wrote in her diary: '[Today] I meant to write about death, only life comes breaking in as usual.'

It was fascinating, with people still laughing and shouting in the drawing-room, to watch that old woman, quite quietly, going to bed alone. She pulled the blind now. The clock began striking. The young man had killed himself; but she did not pity him; with the clock striking the hour, one, two, three, she did not pity him, with all this going on. There! the old lady had put out her light! the whole house was dark now with this going on, she repeated, and the words came to her, Fear no more the heat of the sun.

Mrs Dalloway

February 18th

1895 – The Marquess of Queensberry left his visiting card at Oscar Wilde's club, with the message: 'For Oscar Wilde posing as a somdomite [sic]'.

The worship of the senses has often, and with much justice, been decried ... But it appeared to Dorian

Gray that the true nature of the senses had never been understood, and that they had remained savage and animal merely because the world had sought to starve them into submission or to kill them by pain, instead of aiming at making them elements of a new spirituality, of which a fine instinct for beauty was to be the dominant characteristic.

OSCAR WILDE, The Picture of Dorian Gray

February 19th

1717 – Birth of David Garrick, theatre manager and famous Shakespearean actor, whose portrayal of Richard III first brought him to the Theatre Royal, Drury Lane.

My conscience hath a thousand several tongues,
And every tongue brings in a several tale,
And every tale condemns me for a villain.

WILLIAM SHAKESPEARE, Richard III

February 20th

1923 – Virginia Woolf recorded that the previous day Vita Sackville West and Harold Nicolson had paid a surprise visit. She wrote: '[Vita] is a pronounced Sapphist & may, thinks Ethel Sands, have her eye on me ... '

Sitting on the floor with her arms round Mrs Ramsay's knees, close as she could get, smiling to think that Mrs Ramsay would never know the reason of that pressure, she imagined how in the chambers of the mind and heart of the woman who was, physically, touching her, were stood, like the treasures in the tombs of kings, tablets bearing sacred inscriptions, which if one could spell them out would teach one everything ... What art was there, known to love or cunning, by which one pressed through into those secret chambers?   *To the Lighthouse*

February 21st

1904 – Sir Leslie Stephen clung to life for one last day. Many years after his death, Virginia Woolf wrote: 'His life would have entirely ended mine. What would have happened? No writing, no books – inconceivable.'

Worshipping proportion, Sir William not only pro-
spered himself but made England prosper, secluded
her lunatics, forbade childbirth, penalised despair,
made it impossible for the unfit to propagate their
views until they, too, shared his sense of proportion ...
so that not only did his colleagues respect him, his
subordinates fear him, but the friends and relations of
his patients felt for him the keenest gratitude.

Mrs Dalloway

Illustration from *Limericks*

February 22nd

1935 – Frederic Manning, Australian poet, novelist and essayist, died in Hampstead at the age of fifty-two. His semi-autobiographical *The Middle Parts of Fortune* is widely considered one of the very finest novels based upon the experiences of warfare.

———

> These are the damned circles Dante trod,
> Terrible in hopelessness,
> But even skulls have their humour,
> An eyeless and sardonic mockery:
> And we,
> Sitting with streaming eyes in the acrid smoke
> That murks our foul, damp billet,
> Chant bitterly, with raucous voices
> As a choir of frogs
> In hideous irony, our patriotic songs.

'Grotesque' from *Poetry of the First World War*

———

February 23rd

1903 – Leo Tolstoy wrote to Percy Redfern of the Manchester Tolstoy Society: 'I think your friend who is against books and reading is quite right ... '

———

She threw herself forward on her hands under the truck ... The candle, by the light of which she had been reading that book filled with anxieties, deceptions, grief and evil, flared up with a brighter light, lit up for her all that had before been dark, crackled, began to flicker, and went out for ever.

Anna Karenina

February 24th

1960 – The press showing took place at the Mermaid Theatre of Shakespeare's *Henry V* in modern dress. 'Battledress and boots ... bangs and screams and whistling shells,' warned Bernard Levin in the *Daily Express*.

I see you stand like greyhounds in the slips,
Straining upon the start. The game's afoot:
Follow your spirit; and upon this charge,
Cry, 'God for Harry, England, and Saint George!'

WILLIAM SHAKESPEARE, *Henry V*

February 25th

1897 – Henry James and Joseph Conrad met for lunch in London. James was fifty-three, Conrad thirty-nine, and afterwards for a while a Jamesian tone was discernible in Conrad's work.

———

Hadn't I been told in all the tones of jealousy and admiration that he had collected, bartered, swindled, or stolen more ivory than all the other agents together? That was not the point. The point was in his being a gifted creature, and that of all his gifts the one that stood out pre-eminently, that carried with it a sense of real presence, was his ability to talk, his words – the gift of expression, the bewildering, the illuminating, the most exalted and the most contemptible, the pulsating stream of light, or the deceitful flow from the heart of an impenetrable darkness.

JOSEPH CONRAD, 'Heart of Darkness' from
Heart of Darkness and Other Stories

February 26th

1935 – Scott Fitzgerald was 'on the wagon'. Like most alcoholics, he defined being on the wagon in different ways; at this time it meant drinking only beer.

———

I was enjoying myself now. I had taken two finger-bowls of champagne, and the scene had changed before my eyes into something significant, elemental and profound.

The Great Gatsby

February 27th

1915 – Rupert Brooke, described by Yeats as 'the handsomest young man in England', prepared to sail with the British Expeditionary Force to the Mediterranean. During the expedition he developed sepsis from an infected mosquito bite and died off the island of Skyros in the Aegean on 23 April. He is buried on the island in an olive grove.

———

These hearts were woven of human joys and cares,
    Washed marvellously with sorrow, swift to mirth.
The years had given them kindness. Dawn was theirs,
    And sunset, and the colours of the earth.
These had seen movement, and heard music; known
    Slumber and waking; loved; gone proudly friended;
Felt the quick stir of wonder; sat alone;
    Touched flowers and furs and cheeks.
                        All this is ended ...

    'The Dead' from *Poetry of the First World War*

February 28th

1916 – Henry James died in London. His funeral took place in Chelsea Old Church where a wall-tablet honouring his memory speaks of him as 'lover and interpreter of the fine amenities, of brave decisions and generous loyalties'. He was cremated at Golders Green Crematorium and his ashes were taken to America.

———

She envied Ralph his dying, for if one were thinking of rest that was the most perfect of all. To cease utterly, to give it all up and not know anything more – this idea was as sweet as the vision of a cool bath in a marble tank, in a darkened chamber, in a hot land.

The Portrait of a Lady

February 29th

1960 – The day after his death, F. S. Flint's obituary appeared in *The Times*. A self-educated poet and translator, he had been described by Ford Madox Ford as 'one of the greatest men and one of the beautiful spirits of the country'.

———

> The young men of the world
> Are condemned to death.
> They have been called up to die
> For the crimes of their fathers ...

'Lament' from
Poetry of the First World War

Illustration from *A Shropshire Lad*

Aubrey Beardsley's cover design
from 'Pierrot's Library'

March 1st

1930 – Virginia Woolf wrote: 'Yesterday I was offered £2,000 to write a life of Boswell ... L[eonard] is writing my polite refusal this moment. I have bought my freedom ... I have actually paid for the power to go to Rodmell and only think of *The Waves*.'

———

The waves massed themselves, curved their backs and crashed. Up spurted stones and shingle. They swept round the rocks, and the spray, leaping high, spattered the walls of a cave that had been dry before, and left pools inland, where some fish stranded lashed its tail as the wave drew back.

The Waves

March 2nd

1930 – D. H. Lawrence died in France. E. M. Forster described him as 'the greatest imaginative novelist of our generation'.

———

He laid sex and those base words for it on the salver of his art and held them up before the consciousness of the world ... and prayed that both might be transmuted to the highest that man could use.

REBECCA WEST

March 3rd

1905 – Arnold Bennett invited Somerset Maugham to tea at his Montmartre flat.

———

He has a very calm almost lethargic demeanour. He took two cups of tea with pleasure and absolutely refused a third; one knew instantly from his tone that nothing would induce him to take a third. He ate biscuits and *gaufrettes* very quickly, almost greedily, one after the other without a pause, and then suddenly stopped. He smoked two cigarettes furiously, in less time than I smoked one, and solidly declined a third. I liked him.

ARNOLD BENNETT

March 4th

1893 – Ewart Alan Mackintosh was born in Brighton. His war poetry has been compared in quality to that of Rupert Brooke. He was killed at the Battle of Cambrai at the age of twenty-four.

———

When you and I are buried
With grasses overhead
The memory of our fights will stand

> Above this bare and tortured land
> We knew ere we were dead ...

'Ghosts of War' from *Poetry of the First World War*

March 5th

1921 – E. M. Forster went on board a ship bound for India to take up a post as private secretary to the Ruler of Dewas. In his lifetime something of an enigma, he told T. E. Lawrence, 'When I die and they write my life they can say Everything.'

The novelist should I think always settle when he starts what is going to happen, what his major event is to be. He may alter this event as he approaches it, indeed he probably will, indeed he probably had better, or the novel becomes tied up and tight.

Writers at Work

March 6th

1888 – Louisa M. Alcott died in her sleep in Boston, aged fifty-five, worn out by looking after her father until his death two days earlier. She is buried in distinguished company at Author's Ridge in Concord.

———

The fever flush and look of pain were gone, and the beloved little face looked so pale and peaceful in its utter repose that Jo felt no desire to weep or to lament. Leaning low over the dearest of her sisters, she kissed the damp forehead, with her heart on her lips, and softly whispered, 'Goodbye, my Beth; Goodbye!'

Little Women

March 7th

1898 – Aubrey Beardsley, 'in my death agony', implored his publisher 'to destroy *all* copies of *Lysistrata* ... By all that is holy *all* obscene drawings.' His appeal was in vain.

———

The moral life of man forms part of the subject-matter of the artist, but the morality of art consists in the perfect use of an imperfect medium.

OSCAR WILDE, Preface to *The Picture of Dorian Gray*

March 8th

1859 – Kenneth Grahame was born in Edinburgh but spent much of his childhood in Cookham Dean on the banks of the Thames.

The Mole was bewitched, entranced, fascinated. By the side of the river he trotted as one trots, when very small, by the side of a man who holds one spellbound by exciting stories; and when tired at last, he sat on the bank, while the river still chattered on to him, a babbling procession of the best stories in the world, sent from the heart of the earth to be told at last to the insatiable sea.

The Wind in the Willows

March 9th

1886 – Jules Verne was shot in the leg by his nephew who, partly as a result, spent the rest of his life in a lunatic asylum.

'You love the sea, captain?'

'Yes, I love it! The sea is the be all and end all! It covers seven-tenths of the planet earth. Its breath is clean and healthy. It's an immense wilderness where a man is never lonely, because he feels life astir on every side ... The sea doesn't belong to tyrants. On its surface they can still exercise their iniquitous claims, battle each other, devour each other, perpetrate every earthly horror. But thirty feet below sea level, their dominion ceases, their influence fades, their power vanishes!

Twenty Thousand Leagues Under the Sea

March 10th

1943 – Death of Laurence Binyon whose famous poem 'For the Fallen' was first published by *The Times* in September 1914.

———

With proud thanksgiving, a mother for her children,
England mourns for her dead across the sea.
Flesh of her flesh they were, spirit of her spirit,
Fallen in the cause of the free ...

They shall not grow old, as we that are left grow old:
Age shall not weary them, nor the years condemn.
At the going down of the sun and in the morning
We will remember them ...

Poetry of the First World War

March 11th

1954 – Frances Partridge reported that at a party of 'good greyheads' E. M. Forster and Duncan Grant greeted each other 'like survivors on the same raft'.

In Morgan Forster's company [there] was no mistaking the flavour of a single sentence of his talk ... he always chose to dress in almost aggressively dim grey clothes, woolly cardigans and cloth caps that would have merged easily into a London fog. I think this was because, like his close friend Sebastian Sprott, Morgan felt much more affinity with the lower than the upper classes, and completely lacked ambition, envy and snobbishness.

FRANCES PARTRIDGE

March 12th

1851 – Wilkie Collins's meeting with Charles Dickens took place in the rooms of John Forster. Forster wrote: 'Wilkie Collins became for all of the rest of the life of Dickens one of his dearest and most valued friends.'

A most extraordinary and startling change passed over her. Her face, at all ordinary times so touching to look at, in its nervous sensitiveness, weakness, and uncertainty, became suddenly darkened by an expression of maniacally intense hatred and fear, which communicated a wild, unnatural force to every feature. Her eyes dilated in the dim evening light, like the eyes of a wild animal. She caught up the cloth that had fallen at her side, as if it had been a living creature that she could kill, and crushed it in both her hands with such convulsive strength that the few drops of moisture left in it trickled down on the stone beneath her.

WILKIE COLLINS, *The Woman in White*

Illustration from *Through the Looking-Glass*

March 13th

1889 – Robert Louis Stevenson wrote to Henry James from the South Seas: 'I am not coming home for another year ... and mean to try to work down among the poisoned arrows.'

Oxen and wain-ropes would not bring me back again to that accursed island; and the worst dreams that ever I have are when I hear the surf booming about its coasts, or start upright in bed, with the sharp voice of Captain Flint still ringing in my ears: 'Pieces of eight! Pieces of eight!'

Treasure Island

March 14th

1883 – Karl Marx died in London of bronchitis and pleurisy. He died a stateless person. Family and friends arranged for him to be buried in Highgate Cemetery; there were no more than eleven mourners at the funeral.

It follows therefore that in proportion as capital accumulates, the lot of the labourer, be his payment high or low, must grow worse ... Accumulation of wealth at one pole is, therefore, at the same time accumulation of misery, agony of toil, slavery, ignorance, brutality, mental degradation, at the opposite pole, i.e. on the side of the class that produces its own product in the form of capital.

Selected Works of Karl Marx and Friedrich Engels

March 15th

1937 – H. P. Lovecraft, American writer mainly for pulp magazines in the sub-genre of 'weird fiction', master of what he called 'cosmic horror', died in Providence, Rhode Island, at the age of forty-six. Since his death he has acquired cult status.

———

That damnable print had been all too faithful; yet it could not carry the full horror which lay in the gigantic actuality. The globular torso – the bubblelike suggestion of a head – the three fishy eyes – the foot-long proboscis – the bulging gills – the monstrous capillation of asp-like suckers – the six sinuous limbs with their black paws and crablike claws – God! the familiarity of that black paw ending in a crablike claw!

'The Horror in the Museum' from
Classic Tales of the Macabre

March 16th

1898 – Death of Aubrey Beardsley, illustrator of Oscar Wilde's *Salome*, in Menton at the age of twenty-five.

Aubrey Beardsley illustration for *Salomé*

He could not help liking the tall, graceful young man who was standing by him. His romantic olive-coloured face and worn expression interested him. There was something in his low, languid voice that was absolutely fascinating. His cool, white, flower-like hands, even, had a curious charm. They moved, as he spoke, like music, and seemed to have a language of their own.

OSCAR WILDE, *The Picture of Dorian Gray*

March 17th

AD 180 – Marcus Aurelius died in Vindobona (Vienna). He was immediately deified and his ashes deposited in Hadrian's mausoleum back in Rome, where they remained until the Visigoth sack of the city in AD 410.

Suppose a man can convince me of error and bring home to me that I am mistaken in thought or act, I shall be glad to alter; for the truth is what I pursue, and no one was ever injured by the truth, whereas he is injured who continues in his own self-deception and ignorance.

Meditations

March 18th

1893 – Wilfred Owen was born in Shropshire into a modest middle-class family.

———

He wasn't a fine-drawn type. There was a full-blooded robustness about him which implied reserves of mental energy and solid ability. Under ordinary conditions it wasn't a spiritual face. It was of the mould which either coarsens or refines itself in later life. I cannot say that I ever saw what is called 'a look of genius' in it. His mouth was resolute and humorous, his eyes long and heavy lidded, quiescent rather than penetrating. They were somewhat sleepy eyes, kind, shrewd, and seldom lit up from within. They seemed, like much else in his personality, to be instinctively guarding the secret sources of his inward power and integrity.

SIEGFRIED SASSOON

March 19th

1821 – Sir Richard Burton, geographer, explorer, translator, writer, soldier, orientalist, cartographer, ethnologist, spy, linguist, poet, fencer and diplomat, was born in Torquay. His policy was, 'Do as thy manhood bids thee do; from none but self expect applause.'

———

This fine description will remind the traveller of the old Haurani towns deserted since the sixth century, which a silly writer miscalled the 'Giant Cities of Bashan'. I have never seen anything weirder than moonlight night in one of these strong places whose masonry is perfect as when first built, the snowy light pouring on the jet-black basalt and the breeze sighing and the jackal wailing in the desert around.

BURTON's footnote to page 301 of *The Arabian Nights*

March 20th

1868 – Birth of Ernest Bramah, the popular and versatile writer who created the characters Kai Lung and Max Carrados and has been credited with the invented Chinese curse: 'May you live in interesting times.'

———

The scullery – a dank and forbidding chamber that almost justified its epithet – in turn led into the kitchen, and the kitchen into the hall. But there were other ways of getting about, for it was an old house with many passages and on various levels. Most of the rooms appeared to have at least two doors. 'I think that the man who built it must have been fond of French farces,' remarked Mr Enderleigh.

'The Two Left Shoes' from *Vintage Detective Stories*

March 21st

1920 – Scribner's Sons finally agreed to publish Scott Fitzgerald's first novel, *This Side of Paradise*, and he immediately cabled Zelda to come to New York and marry him.

———

So, while more or less fortunate little rich boys were defying governesses on the beach at Newport, or being spanked or tutored or read to … Amory was biting

acquiescent bellboys in the Waldorf, outgrowing a
natural repugnance to chamber music and sym-
phonies, and deriving a highly specialised education
from his mother.

This Side of Paradise

March 22nd

1921 – E. W. Hornung, famous for being the author
of a series of novels about his creation, Raffles, 'the
gentleman thief', and for being the brother-in-law of
Sir Arthur Conan Doyle, died in the South of France
at the age of fifty-four.

It was not the dark life we led together, still less its
base rewards; it was the man himself, his gaiety, his
humour, his dazzling audacity, his incomparable
courage and resource. And a very horror of turning to
him again in mere need or greed set the seal on my
first angry resolution. But the anger was soon gone out
of me, and when at length Raffles bridged the gap by
coming to me, I rose to greet him almost with a shout.

'Out of Paradise' from *Vintage Detective Stories*

March 23rd

1918 – T. P. Cameron Wilson, poet and novelist, was presumed killed in battle. He has no known grave.

The magpies in Picardy
Are more than I can tell.
They flicker down the dusty roads
And cast a magic spell
On the men who march through Picardy,
Through Picardy to Hell ...

'Magpies in Picardy' from *Poetry of the First World War*

March 24th

1928 – Severely depressed by the death of her sister, Charlotte Mew committed suicide by drinking Lysol. Her poetry spanned the divide between Victorianism and modernism.

Not yet will those measureless fields be green again
Where only yesterday the wild sweet blood of
        wonderful youth was shed;
There is a grave whose earth must hold too long,
        too deep a stain,
Though for ever over it we may speak as proudly
        as we may tread ...

'The Cenotaph' from *Poetry of the First World War*

March 25th

1839 – Charles Dickens took a three-year lease on 48 Doughty Street and set up home with his new wife Catherine and their first child, Charley.

I doubt whether two young birds could have known less about keeping house than I and my pretty Dora did. We had a servant, of course. She kept house for us ... Our treasure was warranted sober and honest. I am therefore willing to believe that she was in a fit when we found her under the boiler; and that the deficient teaspoons were attributed to the dustman.

David Copperfield

March 26th

1859 – A. E. Housman, brilliant Latin scholar and celebrated poet with a strong aversion to public acclaim, was born into a middle-class family in Worcestershire, over the border from Shropshire.

> Into my heart an air that kills
>   From yon far country blows:
> What are those blue remembered hills,
>   What spires, what farms are those?
>
> That is the land of lost content,
>   I see it shining plain,
> The happy highways where I went
>   And cannot come again.

from *A Shropshire Lad*

March 27th

1938 – 'Mr Maugham anatomises emotion,' wrote Elizabeth Bowen in the *New Statesman*. '[but] what a writer he is!'

———

They tried to bar my way, but I pushed them aside. I knew where the private rooms were. Someone clung to my arm, but I shook him off. I vaguely understood that the doctor had given instructions that no one was to go into the room. I didn't care about that. There was an orderly at the door; he put out his arm to prevent me from passing. I swore at him and told him to get out of my way. I suppose I made a row, I was beside myself; the door was opened and the doctor came out.

'The Book-Bag' from
Best Short Stories of Somerset Maugham

March 28th

1941 – Virginia Woolf put on her overcoat, filled its pockets with stones, walked into the River Ouse and drowned herself. In a letter for Leonard she left on the mantelpiece she said: 'I owe all the happiness of my life to you.'

———

Like all her friends, I miss her greatly – I knew her ever since she started writing. But this is a personal matter, and I am sure that there is no case for lamentation here, or for the obituary note. Virginia Woolf got through an immense amount of work, she gave acute pleasure in new ways, she pushed the light of the English language a little further against darkness.

E. M. FORSTER

March 29th

1900 – Rudyard Kipling was present at the battle of Karee Siding, his first exposure to serious fighting in the Boer War.

This is the Elephant's Child
having his nose pulled by the Crocodile. He is much surprised and astonished and hurt, and he is talking through his nose and saying, 'Led go! You are hurtig be!' He is pulling very hard, and so is the Crocodile; but the Bi-Coloured-Python-Rock-Snake is hurrying through the water to help the Elephant's Child. All that black stuff is the banks of the great grey-green, greasy Limpopo River (but I am not allowed to paint these pictures), and the bottly tree with the twisty roots and the eight leaves is one of the fever trees that

grow there. Underneath the truly picture are shadows of African animals walking into an African ark. There are two lions, two ostriches, two oxen, two camels, two sheep, and two other things that look like rats, but I think they are rock-rabbits. They don't mean anything. I put them in because I thought they looked pretty. They would look very fine if I were allowed to paint them.

Just So Stories

March 30th

1820 – Anna Sewell was born in Great Yarmouth into a devoutly Quaker family. An accident when she was fourteen left her virtually unable to walk for the rest of her life.

A short time after this a cart with a dead horse in it passed our cab-stand. The head hung out of the cart tail, the lifeless tongue was slowly dropping blood; and the sunken eyes I – but I can't speak of them, the sight was too dreadful. It was a chestnut horse with a long, thin neck. I saw a white streak down the forehead. I believe it was Ginger; I hoped it was, for then her troubles would be over. Oh! if men were more merciful, they would shoot us before we came to such misery.

Black Beauty

March 31st

1941 – Vita Sackville-West received the news that Virginia Woolf had drowned herself. In her diary, Vita described seeing Leonard at Rodmell a week later.

He was having his tea – just one teacup on the table where they always had tea. The house full of his flowers and all Virginia's things lying about as usual. He said, Let us go somewhere more comfortable, and took me up to her sitting-room. There was her needle-work on a chair and all her coloured wools hanging over a sort of little towel-horse she had made for them. Her thimble on the table. Her scribbling-block with her writing on it. The window from which one can see the river ...

April 1st

1875 – Edgar Wallace was born in Greenwich and entrusted by his single mother to the care of a Billingsgate fishmonger and his wife. At the height of Wallace's success, Somerset Maugham asked Edith Wharton what she thought of his work.

———

'Who is Edgar Wallace?' she replied.
'Do you never read thrillers?'
'No.'
Never has a monosyllable contained more frigid displeasure ... her eyes wandered away and a little forced smile slightly curled her lips.
'I am afraid it's getting late,' said Mrs Wharton.

SOMERSET MAUGHAM

———

April 2nd

1855 – Charlotte Brontë was buried in the family vault under Haworth church; she had died of hyperemesis gravidarum – excessive vomiting during pregnancy – at the age of thirty-eight.

———

[Mr Rochester] cannot now see very distinctly: he cannot read or write much; but he can find his way without being led by the hand ... When his first-born was put into his arms, he could see that the boy had inherited his own eyes, as they once were – large, brilliant, and black.

Jane Eyre

April 3rd

1991 – Grahame Greene died in a private hospital room in Switzerland, having received the last rites from a Spanish priest. He was eighty-six. Kingsley Amis said: 'He will be missed all over the world. Until today he was our greatest living novelist.'

To throw away the gun was a betrayal; it would be an act of cowardice: it would mean that she chose never to see him again for ever. Moral maxims dressed in pedantic priestly tones remembered from old sermons, instructions, confessions – 'you can plead for him at the throne of Grace' – came to her like unconvincing insinuations. The evil act was the honest act, the bold and the faithful – it was only lack of courage, it seemed to her, that spoke so virtuously. She put the gun up to her ear ...

Brighton Rock

April 4th

1915 – Rupert Brooke's poem 'The Soldier' was read from the pulpit of St Paul's Cathedral. He died less than three weeks later.

———

If I should die, think only this of me:
    That there's some corner of a foreign field
That is for ever England. There shall be
    In that rich earth a richer dust concealed;
A dust whom England bore, shaped, made aware,
    Gave, once, her flowers to love, her ways to roam,
A body of England's, breathing English air,
    Washed by the rivers, blest by suns of home ...

from *First World War Poetry*

April 5th

1941 – Chips Channon wrote in his diary: 'Virginia Woolf is dead, a grey highly-strung woman of dignity and charm. She ... did much indirectly to make England so Left.'

———

Somerset Maugham and Virginia Woolf were walking up Whitehall when a couple of bombers came over. '[I] shouted at her to take cover but in the noise she couldn't hear,' Maugham recalled. 'She made no attempt to take cover but stood in the middle of the road and threw her arms into the air. She appeared to be worshipping the flashing sky. It was a most weird sight to watch her there, lit up now and then by the flashes from the guns.'

April 6th

1933 – Graham Greene bought 'a sweet long-haired tabby kitten' in Bond Street for his wife and 'caught the 6.05 home, the kitten in a cardboard box'.

He sniffed with contempt the tainted air. 'You drink too much.' He went to the window and threw it open on the vista of grey wall. A leather-jacket buzzed up the pane and the Boy caught it in his hand. It vibrated like a tiny watch-spring in his palm. He began to pull off the legs and wings one by one. 'She loves me,' he said, 'she loves me not.'

Brighton Rock

April 7th

1935 – Ernest Hemingway sent their publisher a note concerning Scott Fitzgerald: 'A strange thing is that in retrospect *Tender is the Night* gets better and better. I wish you would tell him I said so.' Fitzgerald pasted it in his scrapbook.

———

On the pleasant shore of the French Riviera, about halfway between Marseilles and the Italian border, stands a large, proud, rose-coloured hotel. Deferential palms cool its flushed façade, and before it stretches a short dazzling beach.

Tender is the Night

April 8th

1917 – R. E. Vernéde, writer and poet, who had enlisted in the Rifle Brigade in 1914 despite being four years over-age, was mortally wounded while leading an assault at Havrincourt.

———

The sun's a red ball in the oak
And all the grass is grey with dew,
Awhile ago a blackbird spoke –
He didn't know the world's askew.

And yonder rifleman and I
Wait here behind the misty trees
To shoot the first man that goes by,
Our rifles ready on our knees ...

'A Listening Post' from
Poetry of the First World War

April 9th

1909 – Good Friday. F. Marion Crawford died in Sorrento from damage to his lungs in Colorado ten years earlier. He had inhaled toxic gases when visiting a glass-smelting works to gather technical information for his novel *Marietta* set in medieval Venice.

And then came the most awful sound of all – a woman's shriek, the unearthly scream of a woman neither dead nor alive, but buried deep for many days. And he, the poor old priest, could only rock himself as he knelt there in the sand, crying aloud his prayers and exorcisms to drown these dreadful sounds.

'For the Blood is the Life' from *Spinechillers*

April 10th

1931 – Kahlil Gibran died in New York City at the age of forty-eight; he was taken to be buried in the Lebanon in accordance with his wishes.

Give your hearts, but not into each other's keeping.
For only the hand of Life can contain your hearts.
And stand together yet not too near together:
For the pillars of the temple stand apart,
And the oak tree and the cypress grow not in
each other's shadow.

The Prophet

April 11th

1925 – F. Scott Fitzgerald's novel *The Great Gatsby* was published; it was a critical but not a financial success.

Fitzgerald is a subject no one has the right to mess up. Nothing but the best will do for him ... He had one of the rarest qualities in all literature ... It's a kind of subdued magic, controlled and exquisite, the sort of thing you get from string quartets.

RAYMOND CHANDLER

April 12th

1924 – Virginia Woolf wrote: 'My rooms are all vast panels of moonrises and prima donna's bouquets' – the work of Vanessa and Duncan Grant.

They are listening to the gramophone; they are eating fruit out of paper bags. They are tossing the skins of bananas, which then sink eel-like, into the river. All they do is beautiful. There are cruets behind them and ornaments; their rooms are full of oars and oleographs but they have turned all to beauty.

The Waves

April 13th

2006 – Muriel Spark died in Tuscany aged eighty-eight. Asked about her relationship with her son, she said, 'I think I know how best to avoid him by now.'

One's prime is elusive. You little girls, when you grow up, must be on the alert to recognise your prime at whatever time of your life it may occur. You must then live it to the full.

The Prime of Miss Jean Brodie

April 14th

1912 – Jacques Futrelle, American mystery writer known as the 'Thinking Machine', went down with the *Titanic*; the ship struck an iceberg just before midnight.

———

Then, when the on-rushing car was a full two hundred yards away, Baker planted himself in the middle of the road and began to swing the lantern. The car seemed, if anything, to be travelling even faster than on the previous night. At a hundred yards Baker began to shout. Still the car did not lessen speed, merely rushed on. Again at the psychological instant Baker jumped. The car whisked by as the chauffeur gave it a dexterous twist to prevent running down the special constable.

'The Phantom Motor Car' from
Vintage Detective Stories

———

April 15th

1843 – Henry James was born in New York City into a wealthy and intellectually distinguished family. From the 'white heat' of his genius sprang phrases such as 'a delicate creature swathed in relative clauses as an invalid in shawls'.

———

'I quite agree – in regard to Griffin's ghost, or whatever it was – that its appearing first to the little boy, at so tender an age, adds a particular touch. But it's not the first occurrence of its charming kind that I know to have been concerned with a child. If the child gives the effect another turn of the screw, what do you say to *two* children – ?'

Prologue to *The Turn of the Screw*

April 16th

1938 – Stressed out in Mexico, Graham Greene lay in bed and read Trollope; at such moments he 'found *The Warden* and *Barchester Towers* reassuring books'.

———

Mr Harding is a small man, now verging on sixty years, but bearing few of the signs of age; his hair is rather grizzled, though not grey; his eye is very mild, but clear and bright, though the double glasses which are held swinging from his hand, unless when fixed upon his nose, show that time has told upon his sight; his hands are delicately white, and both hands and feet are small; he always wears a black frock coat, black knee-breeches and black gaiters, and somewhat scandalises some of his more hyper-clerical brethren by a black neck-handkerchief.

ANTHONY TROLLOPE, *The Warden*

April 17th

1919 – Virginia Woolf wrote that she felt 'a little doubtful when I find a cheap ready-made young woman out of an office in Oxford Street & lodging in Harrow enthusiastic about *Robinson Crusoe* ... '

It happened one day, about noon, going towards my boat, I was exceedingly surprised with the print of a man's naked foot on the shore, which was very plain to be seen in the sand. I stood like one thunderstruck, or as if I had seen an apparition.

DANIEL DEFOE, *Robinson Crusoe*

86

April 18th

1868 – Dickens's final appearance of his second visit to the United States was at a banquet the American Press held in his honour at Delmonico's.

———

He might not have made this journey if he could have foreseen the events of a few days ... The frightful deeds that were to be soon done were probably unimagined at that time in the brains of the doers. How could they have a place in the shadowy conceptions of a gentle mind?

A Tale of Two Cities

April 19th

1882 – Charles Darwin died, aged seventy-three, at his home, Down House, in Kent. By popular consensus he was buried in Westminster Abbey where his ashes are kept in a private place for fear of vandals.

———

When we reflect on this struggle, we may console ourselves with the full belief that the war of nature is not incessant, that no fear is felt, that death is generally prompt and that the vigorous, the healthy and the happy survive and multiply.

The Origin of Species

April 20th

1912 – Bram Stoker died in London. Born and educated in Dublin, he had started out in the Civil Service there but later turned to literature and came to London to partner Henry Irving in running the Lyceum Theatre.

———

There lay the count, but looking as if his youth had been half-renewed, for the white hair and moustache were changed to dark iron-grey; the cheeks were fuller, and the white skin seemed ruby-red underneath; the mouth was redder than ever, for on the lips were gouts of fresh blood, which trickled from the corners of the mouth and ran over the chin and neck. Even the deep, burning eyes seemed set amongst swollen flesh, for the lids and pouches underneath were bloated. It seemed as if the whole awful creature were simply gorged with blood; he lay like a filthy leech, exhausted with his repletion.

Dracula

April 21st

1816 – Charlotte Brontë, the eldest of the three Brontë sisters who survived into adulthood, was born in her father's parish of Thornton-le-Dale in the West Riding of Yorkshire.

———

'He would send for the baby; though I entreated him rather to put it out to nurse and pay for its maintenance. I hated it the first time I set my eyes on it – a sickly, whining, pining thing! It would wail in its cradle all night long – not screaming heartily like any other child, but whimpering and moaning. Reed pitied it; and he used to nurse it and notice it as if it had been his own ... In his last illness, he had it brought continually to his bedside; and but an hour before he died, he bound me by vow to keep the creature.'

Jane Eyre

April 22nd

1616 – Death in Madrid of Miguel de Cervantes, Spanish novelist, poet and playwright, author of the first modern European novel, one of the funniest and most tragic books ever written.

In a certain village in La Mancha ... there lived not long ago a gentleman – one of those who have always a lance in the rack, an ancient shield, a lean hack and a greyhound for coursing. His habitual diet consisted of a stew, more beef than mutton, of hash most nights, boiled bones on Saturdays, lentils on Fridays, and a young pigeon as a Sunday treat.

Don Quixote

April 23rd

1616 – St George's Day. Death of William Shakespeare, English poet and playwright, who is widely
regarded as the greatest writer in the English
language and the world's pre-eminent dramatist. It
was the same day on which he was born in 1564.

———

Who steals my purse, steals trash: 'tis
                          something, nothing;
'Twas mine, 'tis his, and has been slave to thousands;
But he that filches from me my good name
Robs me of that which not enriches him
And makes me poor indeed.

WILLIAM SHAKESPEARE, *Othello*

April 24th

1816 – Lord Byron left England, never to return.

———

I'm in the middle of [Byron's] *Don Juan* (about the
fourth time); I do think it's one of the greatest things
from every point of view, poetry, politics and sense,
as well as wit, in the English language. I'd far rather
Paradise Lost disappear than *Don Juan*.

GRAHAM GREENE

April 25th

1878 – Anna Sewell died just five months after the publication of *Black Beauty*, one of the best-selling books of all time.

———

'I felt my whole spirit set against him, and I began to kick, and plunge, and rear as I had never done before; we had a regular fight. For a long time he stuck to the saddle and punished me cruelly with his whip and spurs; but my blood was thoroughly up, and I cared for nothing he could do if only I could get him off.'

April 26th

1856 – Charles Dodgson (Lewis Carroll) encountered four-year-old Alice Liddell for the first time.

The Caterpillar and Alice looked at each other for some time in silence: at last the Caterpillar took the hookah out of its mouth, and addressed her in a languid, sleepy voice.

'Who are *you*?' said the Caterpillar ...

Alice replied, rather shyly, 'I – I hardly know, sir, just at present – at least I know who I *was* when I got up this morning, but I think I must have been changed several times since then.'

Alice in Wonderland

April 27th

1817 – In her 'last will & testament' Jane Austen wrote that she left 'to my dearest Sister Cassandra Eliz^th everything of which I may die possessed'.

———

I often want to criticise Jane Austen, but her books madden me so that I can't conceal my frenzy from my reader; and therefore I have to stop every time I begin. Every time I read *Pride and Prejudice* I want to dig her up and hit her over the skull with her own shin-bone.

MARK TWAIN

April 28th

1849 – Fyodor Dostoevsky and several of his fellow 'conspirators', were imprisoned for sedition in the Peter and Paul Fortress in St Petersburg.

———

'Imagine that you are creating a fabric of human destiny with the object of making men happy in the end ... but that it was essential and inevitable to torture to death only one tiny creature – that baby beating its breast with its fist, for instance – and to found that edifice on its unavenged tears, would you consent to be the architect on those conditions?'

The Brothers Karamazov

April 29th

1930 – Virginia Woolf recorded: 'And I have just finished, with this very nib-full of ink, the last sentence of *The Waves*. Yes, it was the greatest stretch of mind I ever knew.'

Leonard told me that there are two great elms at Rodmell which she always called Leonard and Virginia ... He is going to bury her ashes under one and have a tablet on the tree with a quotation – the one about 'Death is the enemy. Against you I will fling myself unvanquished and unyielding. O Death!' [the last lines of *The Waves*].

VANESSA BELL

April 30th

1934 – Ernest Hemingway wrote to publisher Maxwell Perkins that Scott Fitzgerald's novel *Tender is the Night* was 'emotionally unsound'. He said: 'Scott ... hasn't truly imagined his characters because he doesn't know what people are like to begin with.'

Her naïveté responded wholeheartedly to the expensive simplicity of the Divers, unaware of its complexity and its lack of innocence, unaware that it was all a selection of quality rather than quantity from the run of the world's bazaar; and that the simplicity of behaviour also, the nursery-like peace and good will, the emphasis on the simpler virtues, was part of a desperate bargain with the gods and had been attained through struggles she could not have guessed at. At that moment the Divers represented externally the exact furthermost evolution of a class, so that most people seemed awkward beside them.

Tender is the Night

Illustration from *Cider with Rosie*

May 1st

1912 – Virginia Stephen discussed Leonard Woolf's proposal of marriage with him in a letter: 'As I told you brutally the other day I feel no physical attraction in you ... yet your caring for me as you do almost overwhelms me.'

———

That was what tortured him, that was what came over him when he saw Clarissa so calm, so cold, so intent on her dress or whatever it was; realising what she might have spared him, what she had reduced him to – a whimpering, snivelling old ass. But women, he thought, shutting his pocket-knife, don't know what passion is. They don't know the meaning of it to men. Clarissa was as cold as an icicle. There she would sit on the sofa by his side, let him take her hand, give him one kiss on the cheek.

Mrs Dalloway

May 2nd

1859 – Jerome K. Jerome was born in Staffordshire but grew up in London. His talent for writing humorous prose made him hugely popular with the reading public and provided the means he needed to become one of the founders of *The Idler* magazine and to set up his own twopenny weekly.

———

We did not know what had happened at first, because the sail shut out the view, but from the nature of the language that rose up upon the evening air, we gathered that we had come into the neighbourhood of human beings, and that they were vexed and discontented.

Three Men in a Boat

May 3rd

1915 – John McCrae's poem 'In Flanders Fields' was written at Ypres. Canadian poet, physician, artist and soldier, he died of pneumonia in France in 1918.

In Flanders fields the poppies blow
Between the crosses, row on row,
    That mark our place; and in the sky
    The larks, still bravely singing, fly
Scarce heard amid the guns below ...

'In Flanders Fields' from *Poetry of the First World War*

May 4th

1969 – Death of Osbert Sitwell in Florence. During the First World War he served reluctantly in the Grenadier Guards and it was in the trenches he wrote his first poetry: 'Some instinct and a combination of feelings not hitherto experienced united to drive me to paper.'

———

> I'd send my sons, if old enough, to France,
> Or help to do my share in other ways.
>
> 'Armchair' from *Poetry of the First World War*

May 5th

1809 – Jane Austen wrote an angry letter to publisher Richard Crosby demanding immediate publication of *Susan* or return of the manuscript. He replied that she could repurchase the manuscript for the ten pounds he had paid her – something she could not afford to do.

———

Whether Lady Susan was or was not happy in her second choice, I do not see how it can ever be ascertained; for who would take her assurance of it on either side of the question? The world must judge from probabilities; she had nothing against her but her husband and her conscience.

Lady Susan

May 6th

1919 – Frank Baum died at the age of sixty-two in Hollywood. Author, actor and independent film-maker, he is today best remembered for his children's fantasy *The Wonderful Wizard of Oz*, to which he wrote thirteen sequels.

———

'All the same,' said the Scarecrow, 'I shall ask for brains instead of a heart; for a fool would not know what to do with a heart if he had one.'

'I shall take the heart,' returned the Tin Woodman; 'for brains do not make one happy, and happiness is the best thing in the world.'

May 7th

1980 – Death of Margaret Postgate Pole, socialist poet and politician. During the First World War, her brother's imprisonment as a conscientious objector led to her belief in pacifism.

———

We came upon him sitting in the sun,
Blinded by war and left. And past the fence
There came young soldiers from the Hand and Flower,
Asking advice of his experience.

And he said this, and that, and told them tales,
And all the nightmares of each empty head
Blew into air; then, hearing us beside,
'Poor chaps, how'd they know what it's like?' he said.

And we stood there, and watched him as he sat,
Turning his sockets where they went away,
Until it came to one of us to ask 'And you're how old?'
'Nineteen, the third of May.'

'The Veteran' from *Poetry of the First World War*

May 8th

1880 – Gustave Flaubert died in Rouen. Afflicted with syphilis, he had told his niece, 'Sometimes I think I'm liquifying like an old Camembert.'

———

And he followed her. The key turned in the lock, and she went straight to the third shelf, so well did her memory guide her, seized the jar, tore out the cork, plunged in her hand, and withdrawing it full of a white powder, she began eating it.

'Stop!' he cried, rushing at her ...

'Ah! it is but a little thing, death!' she thought. 'I shall fall asleep and all will be over.'

Madame Bovary

Illustration from *Peter Pan*

May 9th

1860 – J. M. Barrie was born into a conservative Calvinist family of small-town Scottish weavers. He became a prolific writer of novels and plays and by the time *Peter Pan* opened on the London stage in 1904 he was firmly established as a popular literary figure.

───────

Then Peter knew that there was not a moment to lose. 'Come,' he cried imperiously, and soared out at once into the night, followed by John and Michael and Wendy.

  Mr and Mrs Darling and Nana rushed into the nursery too late. The birds were flown.

Peter Pan

May 10th

1848 – Charles Dickens in a letter to Thomas Beard mentioned the behaviour of the family dog: 'Timber is giving such frightful and horribly unnatural tokens of virility, in connexion with an insignificant, drivelling, blear-eyed little tame rabbit of the female gender, that I am in constant expectation of a litter of monsters.'

───────

The animal looked up into his master's face while these preparations were making; whether his instinct apprehended something of their purpose, or the robber's sidelong look at him was sterner than ordinary, he skulked a little farther in the rear than usual, and cowered as he came more slowly along ...

'Do you hear me call? Come here!' cried Sikes.

Oliver Twist

May 11th

1915 – John Middleton Murry had grown so to dislike D. H. Lawrence's wife Frieda that he wrote his plan was to 'see if I can urge him to the point of leaving her'. Lawrence came to consider him 'a dirty little worm'.

———

He writes of his characters as though they were animals circling round each other; and on this sub-human plane no human destinies can be decided ... Life, as Mr Lawrence shows it to us, is not worth living; it is mysteriously degraded by a corrupt mysticism. Mr Lawrence would have us back to the slime from which we rose.

JOHN MIDDLETON MURRY

Illustration from *Oliver Twist*

May 12th

1967 – John Masefield, Poet Laureate from 1930, died. After his ashes had been placed in Poets' Corner a verse was found addressed to his executors begging that his ashes be scattered 'in secret into running water' with no ceremony whatsoever.

———

How still this quiet cornfield is tonight!
By an intenser glow the evening falls,
Bringing, not darkness, but a deeper light;
Among the stooks a partridge covey calls ...

And silence broods like spirit on the brae,
A glimmering moon begins, the moonlight runs
Over the grasses of the ancient way
Rutted this morning by the passing guns.

'August 1914' from *Poetry of the First World War*

_____

_____

_____

_____

_____

May 13th

1997 – Laurie Lee died at eighty-two in Slad near his childhood home and is buried in the village churchyard.

———

The murder and the drowning were long ago, but to me they still loom large; the sharp death-taste, tooth-edge of violence, the yielding to the water of that despairing beauty, the indignant blood in the snow. They occurred at a time when the village was the world and its happenings all I knew.

Cider with Rosie

Illustration from *Cider with Rosie*

May 14th

1927 – Ottaline Morrell wrote of *To the Lighthouse*: 'The beauty of it is overwhelming especially "Time Passes" ... All these pages marked & marked for they seem to me some of the loveliest pages in English prose.'

When darkness fell, the stroke of the lighthouse, which had laid itself with such authority upon the carpet in the darkness, tracing its pattern, came now in the softer light of spring mixed with moonlight gliding gently as if it laid its caress and lingered stealthily and looked and came lovingly again.

To the Lighthouse

May 15th

1856 – Frank Baum was born in Chittenango, New York, of German, Scottish and English ancestry. A daydreamer as a child, he became a highly enterprising publisher of specialist journals before concentrating on his writing and his talent for theatre. Sadly it was twenty years after his death that *The Wizard of Oz* was made into an immensely successful and enduringly popular Hollywood film starring Judy Garland.

As for the fantasy, it weighs like a pound of fruitcake soaking wet.

OTIS FERGUSON

May 16th

1880 – George Eliot married John Cross, a man twenty years younger than herself who during their honeymoon in Venice inexplicably jumped or fell from their hotel balcony into the Grand Canal.

If youth is the season of hope, it is often so only in the sense that our elders are hopeful about us; for no age is so apt as youth to think its emotions, partings, and resolves are the last of their kind. Each crisis seems final, simply because it is new.

Middlemarch

May 17th

1947 – The eve of the day on which Evelyn Waugh took tea with Max Beerbohm, whom he afterwards described as 'a delicious little old dandy, very quick in mind still ... A touch of Ronnie Knox and of Conrad and of Harold Acton ... '

Zuleika had begun her performance. She was producing the Barber's Pole from her mouth. And it was to her that the Duke's heart went suddenly out in tenderness and pity. He forgot her levity and vanity – her wickedness, as he had inwardly called it. He thrilled with that intense anxiety which comes to a man when he sees his beloved offering to the public an exhibition of her skill, be it in singing, acting, dancing or any other art.

MAX BEERBOHM, *Zuleika Dobson*

May 18th

1900 – Sir Basil Thomson, British Intelligence officer, prison governor and colonial administrator, set seal to the establishment of the British Protectorate of Tonga. He wrote for relaxation in his spare time.

He had added chestnut hair to his reconstruction of the head, and colour to the cheeks; in her current state she must certainly have been very trying to live with, even when covered with a sheet.

'The Hanover Court Murder' from
Vintage Detective Stories

May 19th

1897 – Oscar Wilde was released from Reading Gaol and left England the following day to spend his last three years in penniless exile.

He felt a wild longing for the unstained purity of his boyhood – his rose-white boyhood ... He knew that he had tarnished himself, filled his mind with corruption, and given horror to his fancy; that he had been an evil influence to others, and had experienced a terrible joy in being so; and that, of the lives that had crossed his own, it had been the fairest and the most full of promise that he had brought to shame.

The Picture of Dorian Gray

May 20th

1956 – Sir Max Beerbohm died in Italy at the age of eighty-three shortly after embarking upon a second marriage. In his youth he always used to say, 'I was always a modest, good-humoured boy. It is Oxford that has made me insufferable.'

You know how, at a concert, a prima donna who has just sung insists on shaking hands with the accompanist, and dragging him forward, to show how beautiful her nature is, into the applause that is for herself alone. And your heart, like mine, has gone out to the wretched victim.

Zuleika Dobson

May 21st

1892 – The poet John Peale Bishop was born in West Virginia. A friend of F. Scott Fitzgerald's, he was the model for Thomas Parke D'Invilliers in Fitzgerald's first novel *This Side of Paradise.*'

> We stood up before day
> and shaved by metal mirrors
> in the faint flame of a faulty candle ...
>
> And each day one died or another
> died: each week we sent out thousands
> that returned by hundreds
> wounded or gassed. And those that died
> we buried close to the old wall
> within a stone's throw of Perigord
> under the tower of the troubadours ...

'In the Dordogne' from *Poetry of the First World War*

May 22nd

1859 – Arthur Conan Doyle was born in Edinburgh to parents of Irish descent. He studied medicine at Edinburgh University and one of his professors, the surgeon Joseph Bell, left a lasting impression. When Doyle decided to try his hand at detective fiction and had to invent a sleuth: 'I thought of my old teacher Joe Bell, of his eagle face, of his curious ways, of his eerie trick of spotting details.'

———

Bell was a very remarkable man in body and mind. He was thin, wiry, dark, with a high-nosed acute face, penetrating grey eyes, angular shoulders and a jerky way of walking. His voice was high and discordant. He was a very skilful surgeon, but his strong point was diagnosis, not only of disease, but of occupation and character.

ARTHUR CONAN DOYLE

May 23rd

1869 – Joseph Conrad, aged eleven, was left an orphan on the death of his father, Apollo Korzeniowski, a political activist and social reformer who belonged to the Polish upper class.

———

This was then the famous and trusty secret agent, so secret that he was never designated otherwise but by the symbol Δ in the late Baron Stott-Wartenheim's official, semi-official and confidential correspondence; the celebrated agent Δ whose warnings had the power to change the schemes and the dates of royal, imperial, grand-ducal journeys, and sometimes cause them to be put off altogether! This fellow!

The Secret Agent

May 24th

1849 – Anne Brontë died of tuberculosis on a visit to Scarborough and is buried in the churchyard over-looking the bay. She was only twenty-nine years old.

———

' "Death is so terrible," he cried, "I cannot bear it! *You* don't know, Helen – you can't imagine what it is, because you haven't it before you; and when I'm buried, you'll return to your old ways and be as happy as ever, and all the world will go on just as busy and merry as if I had never been; while I – " He burst into tears.

' "You needn't let *that* distress you," I said; "we shall all follow you soon enough." '

The Tenant if Wildfell Hall

May 25th

1915 – Julian Grenfell lay dying of wounds in a hospital in Boulogne. Two days later, after his death, *The Times* published his most famous poem 'Into Battle'.

The thundering line of battle stands,
    And in the air death moans and sings;
But Day shall clasp him with strong hands,
    And Night shall fold him in soft wings.

'Into Battle' from *Poetry of the First World War*

May 26th

1962 – Wilfrid Wilson Gibson, one of the first Georgian poets, died. He had been a close friend and literary executor of Rupert Brooke.

On the low table by the bed
Where it was set aside last night,
Beyond the bandaged lifeless head,
It glitters in the morning light;

And as the hours of watching pass,
I cannot sleep, I cannot think,
But only gaze upon the glass
Of water that he could not drink.

'Mark Anderson' from *Poetry of the First World War*

May 27th

1894 – Dashiell Hammett was born in Maryland. 'Dashiell' was his mother's maiden name, anglicised from the French De Chiel.

Hammett took murder out of the Venetian vase and dropped it into the alley; it doesn't have to stay there for ever, but it was a good idea ... Hammett gave murder back to the kind of people who do it for a reason, not just to provide a corpse; and with the means at hand, not with hand-wrought duelling pistols, curare and tropical fish.

RAYMOND CHANDLER

May 28th

1917 – Lytton Strachey met Robert Graves.

For instance there is the youth Graves, with one lung shot away, keeping himself going on strychnine, and with strange concealed thoughts which only very occasionally poke up through his schoolboy jocularities. Terribly tragic I thought. I found him (I need hardly say) attractive – tall and olive-brown complexioned, with a broken nose and broken teeth (the result of boxing) – dark hair and eyes.

LYTTON STRACHEY

May 29th

1874 – G. K. Chesterton was born on Campden Hill, Kensington. A character larger than life in every sense, he was extremely clumsy as a child and possibly had undiagnosed dyspraxia. His most famous creation, Father Brown, is a small, unobtrusive Catholic priest with a highly developed understanding of the criminal mind.

———

A man generally makes a small scene if he finds salt in his coffee; if he doesn't, he has some reason for keeping quiet. I changed the salt and sugar, and *you* kept quiet. A man generally objects if his bill is three times too big. If he pays it, he has some motive for passing unnoticed. I altered your bill, and *you* paid it.'

'The Blue Cross' from
Father Brown: Selected Stories

May 30th

1915 – Charles Sorley arrived at the Western Front and was shot in the head at the Battle of Loos 116 days later. John Masefield said he was the greatest loss of all the poets killed during the Great War.

———

When you see millions of the mouthless dead
Across your dreams in pale battalions go,
Say not soft things as other men have said,

That you'll remember. For you need not so.
Give them not praise. For, deaf, how should they know
It is not curses heaped on each gashed head?
Nor tears. Their blind eyes see not your tears flow.
Nor honour. It is easy to be dead.
Say only this, 'They are dead' ...

> 'When you see millions of the mouthless dead'
> from *Poetry of the First World War*

May 31st

1917 – Reviewing Siegfried Sassoon's *The Old Huntsman and Other Poems*, Virginia Woolf wrote: 'Here we have evidence of the gift of being a poet.'

———

'Good-morning; good-morning!' the General said
When we met him last week on our way to the Line.
Now the soldiers he smiled at are most of 'em dead,
And we're cursing his staff for incompetent swine.
'He's a cheery old card,' grunted Harry to Jack
As they slogged up to Arras with rifle and pack.

*　　*　　*

But he did for them both by his plan of attack.

> 'The General' from *Poetry of the First World War*

June 1st

1878 – John Masefield, distinguished poet and prolific writer of novels, plays and children's fiction was born in Herefordshire. His aunt sent him to sea to break his addiction to reading.

I had a rather moving experience at Masefield's. At his little theatre he made a long eulogy on my work & myself – very embarrassing – & then five girls with beautiful voices recited my lyrics for three quarters of an hour. I do not think the whole audience could hear but to me it was strangely overwhelming ...

W. B. YEATS

June 2nd

1840 – At eight o'clock on a Tuesday morning, Thomas Hardy was born in a tiny village in Dorset.

The baby's offence against society in coming into the world was forgotten by the girl-mother; her soul's desire was to continue that offence by preserving the life of the child. However, it soon grew clear that the hour of emancipation for that little prisoner of the flesh was to arrive earlier than her worst misgivings had conjectured.

Tess of the D'Urbervilles

June 3rd

1924 – Franz Kafka died at a sanatorium near Vienna; his tuberculous condition made it too painful to eat and he died of starvation. He was only forty. He left his friend Max Brod instructions to destroy his unpublished writings, but for the sake of posterity Brod disregarded them.

Someone must have been spreading lies about Josef K for without having done anything wrong he was arrested one morning ... At once there was a knock at the door and a man he had never seen in the flat before came in. He was slim and yet strongly built;

he wore a well-fitting black suit which was like a travelling outfit in that it had various pleats, pockets, buckles, buttons and a belt, and as a result (although one could not quite see what it was for) it seemed eminently practical.

The Trial

___

June 4th

1875 – The *San Francisco Chronicle* reported the attempted suicide of Flora Wellman, who had shot herself in despair at finding herself pregnant and abandoned. The child she subsequently gave birth to was Jack London.

___

He had killed man, the noblest game of all, and he had killed in the face of the law of club and fang. He sniffed the bodies curiously. They had died so easily. It was harder to kill a husky dog than them. They were no match at all, were it not for

their arrows and spears and clubs. Thenceforward he
would be unafraid of them except when they bore in
their hands their arrows, spears and clubs.

The Call of the Wild

June 5th

1910 – William Sydney Porter, the hugely popular
writer of short stories whose pen name was O. Henry,
died in New York City at the age of forty-seven. His
stories often have a twist in the tale – a device which
came to be called an 'O. Henry ending'.

'Mr Behrman died of pneumonia today in the
hospital. He was ill only two days. The janitor found
him the morning of the first day in his room down-
stairs helpless with pain. His shoes and clothing were
wet through and icy cold. They couldn't imagine
where he had been on such a dreadful night ... '

'The Last Leaf' from *Classic Tales of the Macabre*

June 6th

1862 – Sir Henry Newbolt, described by Virginia Woolf as 'a slim grey-headed weasel', was born in Staffordshire.

————

I was out early today, spying about
From the top of a haystack – such a lovely morning –
And when I mounted again to canter back
I saw across a field in the broad sunlight
A young Gunner Subaltern, stalking along
With a rook-rifle held at the ready, and –
                would you believe it? –
A domestic cat, soberly marching beside him.

'A Letter from the Front' from
Poetry of the First World War

June 7th

1970 – E. M. Forster died of a stroke at the age of ninety-one in the Coventry home of his long-time friend Bob Buckingham. His abiding philosophy was that the individual need 'only connect' to lead a fairly untroubled social existence.

————

Will all the poetry in the world satisfy the manhood of Forster, when Forster knows that his implicit manhood is to be satisfied by nothing but immediate physical action? He tries to dodge himself – the sight is pitiful.

D. H. LAWRENCE

June 8th

1870 – Charles Dickens spent the day working on *The Mystery of Edwin Drood*. That evening he collapsed and the next day he died.

Not much of Dickens will live, because it has so little correspondence to life. He was the incarnation of cockneydom, a caricaturist who aped the moralist; he should have kept to short stories.

GEORGE MEREDITH

Illustration from *Three Men in a Boat*

June 9th

1865 – Charles Dickens, travelling with Ellen Ternan and her mother, was involved in a rail crash between Folkestone and Charing Cross.

On Friday, the Ninth of June in the present year, Mr and Mrs Boffin (in their manuscript dress of receiving Mr and Mrs Lammle at breakfast) were on the South-Eastern Railway with me in a terribly destructive accident. When I had done what I could to help others,

I climbed back into my carriage – nearly turned over a viaduct, and caught aslant upon the turn – to extricate the worthy couple. They were much soiled, but otherwise unhurt. The same happy result attended

Miss Bella Wilfer on her wedding day, and Mr Riderhood inspecting Bradley Headstone's red neckerchief as he lay asleep. I remember with devout thankfulness that I can never be much nearer parting company with my readers for ever than I was then, until there shall be written against my life the two words with which I have this day closed this book – THE END.

Postscript to Our Mutual Friend

June 10th

1802 – Dorothy Wordsworth recorded that Coleridge came over with 'a sack-full of books, etc.' On the way he had been 'attacked by a cow'. Dorothy kept her *Journals* at Grasmere at the time her brother and Coleridge were composing the *Lyrical Ballads*. In 1916, Robert Graves and Siegfried Sassoon were planning a joint publication along the same lines.

[Sassoon] had seen the last issue of *The Nation*, and commented what fun it was for us two to appear as a military duet in a pacifist organ. 'You and me, the poets who mean to work together someday and scandalise the jolly old Gosses and Stracheys.'

ROBERT GRAVES, Goodbye to All That

June 11th

1815 – Birth in Lambeth of Hablot Knight Browne, famous as Phiz, illustrator of books by Charles Dickens. He chose the name 'Phiz' to harmonise with Dickens's 'Boz'. He illustrated ten of Dickens's novels but worked for many other writers and contributed drawings to *Punch* during his long career.

Illustration from *Nicholas Nickleby*

June 12th

1842 – Death of Dr Thomas Arnold, famous reforming educationalist and headmaster of Rugby School, who was idealised as the perfect schoolmaster by Thomas Hughes in *Tom Brown's Schooldays*.

———

'Very well then, let's roast him,' cries Flashman, and catches hold of Tom by the collar; one or two boys hesitate, but the rest join in. East seizes Tom's arm and tries to pull him away, but is knocked back by one of the boys, and Tom is dragged along struggling. His shoulders are pushed against the mantelpiece, and he is held by main force before the fire, Flashman drawing his trousers tight by way of extra torture.

Tom Brown's Schooldays

June 13th

1865 – W. B. Yeats was born an Anglo-Irishman in County Dublin but the family soon moved to Sligo, his 'county of the heart', his childhood and spiritual home. The greatest lyric poet that Ireland has produced and the leader of the Irish Literary Revival, he was 'one of those few ... who are part of the consciousness of an age which cannot be understood without them' (T. S. Eliot)

———

Much did I rage when young,
Being by the world oppressed,
But now with flattering tongue
It speeds the parting guest.

'Youth and Age' from *Collected Poems of W. B. Yeats*

June 14th

1936 – G. K. Chesterton died of congestive heart failure at his home in Beaconsfield. A requiem mass was held for him in Westminster Cathedral.

He raised his eyes and saw through the veil of incense smoke and of twinkling lights that Benediction was drawing to its end while the procession waited. The sense of accumulated riches of time and tradition pressed past him like a crowd moving in rank after rank, through unending centuries; and high above them all, like a garland of unfading flames, like the sun of our mortal midnight, the great monstrance blazed against the darkness of the vaulted shadows, as it blazed against the black enigma of the universe. For some are convinced that this enigma also is an insoluble problem. And others have equal certitude that it has but one solution.

'The Insoluble Problem'
from *Father Brown: Selected Stories*

June 15th

1904 – James Joyce wrote to Nora Barnacle asking to see her again – 'if you have not forgotten me!'

———

[H]e kissed me under the Moorish wall and I thought well as well him as another and then I asked him with my eyes to ask again yes and then he asked me would I yes to say yes my mountain flower and first I put my arms around him yes and drew him down to me so he could feel my breasts all perfume yes and his heart was going like mad and yes I said yes I will Yes.

Ulysses

June 16th

1904 – Bloomsday – the day during which the events in James Joyce's novel *Ulysses* took place.

———

Mr Leopold Bloom ate with relish the inner organs of beasts and fowls. He liked thick giblet soup, nutty gizzards, a stuffed roast heart, liver slices fried with crust-crumbs, fried hencod's roes. Most of all he liked grilled mutton kidneys which gave to his palate a fine tang of faintly scented urine.

Ulysses

June 17th

1937 – 'Sir James Barrie lies a-dying,' wrote Chips
Channon. 'I have always disliked the little man and
thought him boorish and petulant ... though he did
add Peter Pan and a few other characters to our
literature.'

Peter was not quite like other boys; but he was afraid at last. A tremor ran through him, like a shudder passing over the sea; but on the sea one shudder follows another till there are hundreds of them, and Peter felt just the one. Next moment he was standing erect on the rock again, with that smile on his face and a drum beating within him. It was saying, 'To die will be an awfully big adventure.'

June 18th

1927 – A letter from her sister in France about being beset by moths at night inspired Virginia Woolf: 'Now the moth will fill out ... the play-poem idea – the idea of some continuous stream ... ' This was the genesis of *The Waves*.

All for a moment wavered and bent in uncertainty and ambiguity, as if a great moth sailing through the room had shadowed the immense solidity of chairs and tables with floating wings.

The Waves

June 19th

1937 – J. M. Barrie died of pneumonia and was buried next to his parents at Kirriemuir in Scotland. He had previously given the rights of *Peter Pan* to Great Ormond Street Hospital.

———

Doctors sometimes draw maps of other parts of you, and your own map can become intensely interesting, but catch them trying to draw a map of a child's mind ... There are zigzag lines on it, just like your temperature on a card ...

Peter Pan

June 20th

1908 – With four of his plays being performed in the West End, Somerset Maugham was hailed by Max Beerbohm in the *Saturday Review* as 'the hero of the year ... [whose] name is a household word even in households where the theatre is held unclean'.

———

She was no longer the cowed drudge of the last days. She was dressed in all her finery, in her white dress, with the high shiny boots over which her fat legs bulged in their cotton stockings ... Her face was painted, her eyebrows were boldly black, and her lips were scarlet.

'Rain' from *Best Short Stories of Somerset Maugham*

June 21st

1888 – Jerome K. Jerome married Ettie Marris and they honeymooned in a 'little boat on the Thames'. Inspired, on their return he began *Three Men in a Boat*.

The order of the procession was as follows: Montmorency, carrying a stick. Two disreputable-looking curs, friends of Montmorency's. George, carrying coats and rugs, and smoking a short pipe. Harris, trying to walk with easy grace, while carrying a bulged-out Gladstone bag in one hand and a bottle of lime-juice in the other. Greengrocer's boy and baker's boy, with baskets. Boots from the hotel, carrying hamper. Confectioner's boy, with basket. Grocer's boy, with basket. Long-haired dog. Cheesemonger's boy, with basket. Odd man, carrying a bag. Bosom companion of odd man, with his hands in his pockets, smoking a short clay. Fruiterer's boy, with basket. Myself, carrying three hats and a pair of boots, and trying to look as if I didn't know it. Six small boys, and four stray dogs.

June 22nd

1898 – Eric Maria Remarque was born into a working-class family in the German city of Osnabrück. At nineteen he was severely wounded on the Western Front. His novel about his war experiences was banned by the Nazis. He died in Switzerland 1948.

The body is still, completely quiet, there is not a single sound, and even the gurgling has stopped, but the eyes are screaming, roaring, all his life has gathered in them and formed itself into an incredible urge to escape, into a terrible fear of death, a fear of me.

All Quiet on the Western Front

June 23rd

1948 – Graham Greene on a visit to Vienna with Carol Reed to work on the film treatment of *The Third Man* went into the Russian Sector: 'The Prater lay smashed and desolate and full of weeds, only the Great Wheel revolving slowly ... '

Harry took a look at the toy landscape ... 'Victims?' he asked. 'Don't be melodramatic, Rollo. Look down there,' he went on, pointing through the window at the people moving like black flies at the base of the Wheel. 'Would you really feel any pity if one of those dots stopped moving – for ever? If I said you can have twenty thousand pounds for every dot that stops, would you really, old man, tell me to keep my money? ... Free of income tax, old man.' He gave his boyish conspiratorial smile. 'It's the only way to save nowadays.'

The Third Man and Other Stories

June 24th

1919 – Memorial service for a somebody – Walter Weedon Grossmith – at St Martin-in-the-Fields.

My first thought was that I had ruptured an artery, and was bleeding to death, and should be discovered, later on, looking like a second Marat, as I remember seeing him in Madame Tussaud's. My second thought was to ring the bell, but remembered there was no bell to ring.  My third was that it was nothing but the enamel paint, which had dissolved with boiling water.

Diary of a Nobody

June 25th

1870 – Erskine Childers was born in Mayfair. He spent much of his childhood in Ireland in the care of his mother's Anglo-Irish landowning family. After leaving Cambridge he worked as a clerk at the House of Commons and pursued his passion for sailing during the long parliamentary recesses.

———

The most studied calculation could not have secured us more favourable conditions for a moment which I had always dreaded – the meeting of Davies and Dollmann. The former, having shortened his sculls, just sat where he was, half turned towards the yacht and looking up at his enemy. No lineament of his own face could have been visible to the latter, while those pitiless green rays – you know their ravaging effect on the human physiognomy – struck full on Dollmann's face ... I feasted with a luxury of superstitious abhorrence on the livid smiling mask that for a few moments stooped peering down towards Davies.

Riddle of the Sands

June 26th

1914 – Laurie Lee was born in Stroud, Gloucestershire, into a bucolic world whose days were numbered.

———

The June grass, among which I stood, was taller than I was, and I wept. I had never been so close to grass before. It towered above me and all around me, each blade tattooed with tiger-skins of sunlight. It was knife-edged, dark, and a wicked green, thick as a forest and alive with grasshoppers that chirped and chattered and leapt through the air like monkeys.

Cider with Rosie

Illustration from *Cider with Rosie*

June 27th

1787 – Edward Gibbon 'wrote the last lines of the last page [of *The Decline and Fall of the Roman Empire*] in a summer house' in his garden. 'It was on the day, or rather the night of 27 June 1787, between the hours of eleven and twelve.'

I will not dissemble the first emotion of joy on the recovery of my freedom, and, perhaps, the establishment of fame. But my pride was soon humbled, and a sober melancholy was spread over my mind, by the idea that I had taken an everlasting leave of an old and agreeable companion, and that whatsoever might be the future of my *History*, the life of the historian must be short and precarious.

EDWARD GIBBON

June 28th

1929 – Edward Carpenter, poet, socialist, philosopher, anthologist and early gay-rights activist, died in Guildford.

And nobody knew whatever on earth
Our present objective and aim were,
And whether the loss and deadly dearth
Of another million lives was worth
Some gains in Mesopotamia.

'Twas insubordination, they said,
And he surely must be crazy …
Yet there he stood, in mien well-bred,
Collected and calm, with clean-cut head,
And looking as fit as a daisy.

And an MC too … so what could they do?

'Lieutenant Tattoon MC' from
Poetry of the First World War

Illustration from *A Shropshire Lad*

June 29th

1956 – The ashes of Sir Max Beerbohm, brought from Genoa, were interred in the crypt of St Paul's Cathedral.

———

But the dullard's envy of brilliant men is always assuaged by the suspicion that they will come to a bad end.

Zuleika Dobson

June 30th

1926 – 'This is the last day of June & finds me in a black despair because Clive [Bell] laughed at my new hat ... & they pulled me down between them, like a hare.' Virginia Woolf declared: ' ... & today has been ruined.'

———

June had drawn out every leaf on the trees. The mothers of Pimlico gave suck to their young. Messages were passing from the Fleet to the Admiralty. Arlington Street and Piccadilly seemed to chafe the very air in the Park and lift its leaves hotly, brilliantly, on waves of that divine vitality which Clarissa loved. To dance, to ride, she had adored all that.

Mrs Dalloway

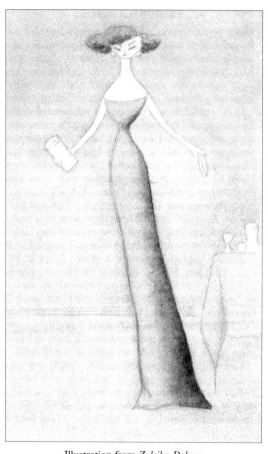

Illustration from *Zuleika Dobson*

July 1st

1896 – Harriet Beecher Stowe died at the age of eighty-five in Hartford, Connecticut, after a lifetime of campaigning, primarily against slavery in the South.

Right on behind they came; and, nerved with strength such as God gives only to the desperate, with one wild cry and flying leap she vaulted sheer over the turbid current by the shore on to the raft of ice beyond. It was a desperate leap – impossible to anything but madness and despair ... With wild cries and desperate energy she leaped to another and still another cake; stumbling – leaping – slipping – springing upwards again! Her shoes were gone – her stockings cut from her feet – while blood marked every step; but she saw nothing, felt nothing, till dimly, as in a dream, she saw the Ohio side.

Uncle Tom's Cabin

July 2nd

1961 – Ernest Hemingway shot himself. In 1936 F. Scott Fitzgerald had described him as 'the most dynamic personality' in the world.

There are no second acts in American lives.

F. SCOTT FITZGERALD

Illustration from *Oliver Twist*

July 3rd

1883 – Franz Kafka was born in Prague, then part of the Austro-Hungarian Empire, into a family of Ashkenazi Jews. Now regarded as one of the greatest novelists of the twentieth century, his fiction explores the alienation of the outsider at odds with authority in situations whose nightmare quality has come to be described as 'Kafkaesque'.

———

Am I now going to demonstrate that not even this trial, which has gone on for a year, has taught me anything? Am I going to depart this life a dim-witted man? Are people going to be able to say about me that at the beginning of the case I wanted to end it, and that now, when it's coming to an end, I want to start it all over again?

The Trial

July 4th

1804 – Nathaniel Hawthorne was born Hathorne but later added the w to his name to disassociate himself from the notorious judge of the Salem witch trials. Successful as a writer in his native Massachusetts, he spent four years towards the end of his life as American consul in Liverpool.

———

The sainted minister in the church! The woman of the scarlet letter in the marketplace! What imagination would have been irreverent enough to surmise that the same scorching stigma was on them both!

The Scarlet Letter

July 5th

1845 – Henry David Thoreau woke to the first day of his life on Walden Pond. He was conducting an experiment in living independently and self-sufficiently away from society.

I wanted to live deep and suck out all the marrow of life, to live so sturdily and Spartan-like as to put to rout all that was not life, to cut a broad swathe and shave close, to drive life into a corner, and reduce it to its lowest terms, and, if it proved to be mean, why then to get the whole and genuine meanness of it, and publish its meanness to the world.

Walden

July 6th

1932 – Kenneth Grahame died, leaving, in the words of Anthony Hope, 'childhood and literature through him the more blest for all time.' His life had been wrecked by the tragic suicide of his son Alastair, whose bedtime stories had been the source of his masterpiece.

Oh my, how cold the water was, and oh, how *very* wet it felt. How it sang in his ears as he went down, down, down! How bright and welcome the sun looked as he rose to the surface coughing and spluttering! How black was his despair when he felt himself sinking again! Then a firm paw gripped him by the back of his neck. It was the Rat, and he was evidently laughing – the Mole could *feel* him laughing, right down his arm and through his paw, and so into his – the Mole's – neck.

The Wind in the Willows

July 7th

1930 – Following a heart attack at the age of seventy-one, Sir Arthur Conan Doyle died, sitting in his basket chair, looking out across his Sussex garden.

'It is my belief, Watson, founded upon my experience, that the lowest and vilest alleys in London do not present a more dreadful record of sin than does the smiling and beautiful countryside.'

'The Copper Beeches' from
The Adventures of Sherlock Holmes

July 8th

1822 – Percy Bysshe Shelley was lost at sea off the coast of Italy. His body was washed ashore ten days later.

Figure a bolt-eyed blue-shirted shockheaded hatless man in a blue overcoat standing goggling at the door at 4.30, on Friday. 'Mrs Woolf? ... I'm Graves.' Everybody stared. He appeared to have been rushing through the air at 60 miles an hour & to have alighted temporarily ... He has a crude likeness to Shelley, save that his nose is a switchback & his lines blurred.

VIRGINIA WOOLF

July 9th

1912 – G. K. Chesterton, famously absent-minded, sent a telegram to his wife: 'Am in Market Harborough. Where ought I to be?' With his flowing cloak, broad-brimmed hat and swordstick, he was a familiar figure and something of a national treasure. A formidable literary force, he influenced contemporaries as diverse as Michael Collins, C. S. Lewis and Mahatma Gandhi with his thrusts and paradoxes.

———

A young man who wishes to remain a sound atheist cannot be too careful of his reading.

Quoted by C. S. Lewis in *Surprised by Joy*

July 10th

1932 – Graham Greene wrote in his diary: 'Finished Ford's novel. What a book ... his complicated time-juggling better than Conrad's ... Ford is as full of life as a flea.'

———

And, when one discusses an affair – a long, sad affair – one goes back, one goes forward. One remembers points that one has forgotten and one explains them all the more minutely since one recognises that one has forgotten to mention them in their proper places and that one may have given, by omitting them, a false impression.

FORD MADOX FORD, *The Good Soldier*

July 11th

1937 – Edith Wharton died in France. She was friends with many literary contemporaries but her meeting with F. Scott Fitzgerald is described as one of the better known failed encounters in the American literary annals.

———

The disappointment was not occasioned by the sentiment ordinarily defined as snobbishness, but by old New York's sense of what was due to it.

EDITH WHARTON, *The Age of Innocence*

Illustration from *Limericks*

Illustration from *The Railway Children*

July 12th

1919 – Virginia Woolf bumped into E. M. Forster at Waterloo Station.

———

I met Morgan Forster on the platform at Waterloo yesterday; a man physically resembling a blue butterfly – I mean by that to describe his transparency & lightness. He had been conveying the luggage of 5 Indians from Deptford to Waterloo; Indians seemed to weigh him down.

VIRGINIA WOOLF

July 13th

1914 – D. H. Lawrence and Frieda Weekly were married at Kensington Registry Office. Katherine Mansfield and John Middleton Murry were witnesses.

———

The two couples went asunder, Ursula clinging to Birkin's arm. When they had gone some distance, she glanced back and saw the young man going beside the full, easy young woman. His trousers sank over his heels, he moved with a sort of slinking evasion ...

And yet he was somewhere indomitable and separate, like a quick, vital rat. He had a queer, subterranean beauty, repulsive too.

D. H. LAWRENCE, *Women in Love*

July 14th

1933 – Graham Greene reported that at a Heinemann garden party L. P. Hartley was to be seen 'sitting in an immaculate overcoat in the warm sun, quiet, affected, exaggeratedly Balliol'.

The Boy paid his threepence and went through the turnstile. He moved rigidly past the rows of deck-chairs four deep where people were waiting for the orchestra to play. From behind he looked younger than he was in his dark thin ready-made suit a little too big for him at the hips, but when you met him face to face he looked older, the slatey eyes were touched with the annihilating eternity from which he had come and to which he went.

Brighton Rock

Illustration from *Cider with Rosie*

July 15th

1954 – Raymond Chandler writing about L. P. Hartley's *The Go-Between* said: 'I started it and dropped it and went back half a dozen times before I got far enough to give a damn about anyone ... Maugham would have done that story to perfection, but he wouldn't have written it through the eyes of a twelve-year-old boy.'

———

I ran through the rain at Mrs Maudsley's side. I did not know that she could run at all; but I could hardly keep up with her, she ran so fast. Her lilac paper bonnet was soon soaked through; it flapped dismally as she ran, then clung to her head, dark and transparent, while the water dripped off the strings ... I could not bear to aid her in her search, and shrank back, crying ... and it was then that we saw them ... I think I was more mystified than horrified; it was Mrs Maudsley's repeated screams that frightened me, and a shadow on the wall that opened and closed like an umbrella.

The Go-Between

July 16th

1930 – Virginia Woolf wrote to Hugh Walpole: 'I like printing in my basement best, almost; no, I like drinking champagne and getting wildly excited. I like driving off to Rodmell on a hot Friday evening and having cold ham on my terrace and smoking a cigar with an owl or two.'

———

'After all, we are not responsible. We are not judges. We are not called upon to torture our fellows with thumbscrews and irons; we are not called upon to mount pulpits and lecture them on pale Sunday afternoons. It is better to look at a rose, or to read Shakespeare as I read him here in Shaftesbury Avenue.'

The Waves

July 17th

1917 – Arnold Bennett wrote to Robert Ross: 'The fact is, my dear Robert, I am much concerned about Sassoon ... I agree with you that he must be a little deranged.'

———

You smug-faced crowds with kindling eye
Who cheer when soldier lads march by,
Sneak home and pray you'll never know
The hell where youth and laughter go.

SIEGFRIED SASSOON, 'Suicide in the Trenches'
from *Poetry of the First World War*

July 18th

1943 – Chipps Channon gave Lord Alfred Douglas lunch in Brighton and found him 'ageing, but still gay and young in manner. He now boasts of his relationship with Wilde, and was fascinating about him and them ... '

———

He was conscious – and the thought brought a gleam of pleasure into his brown agate eyes – that ... to a large extent the lad was his own creation. He had made him premature. That was something. Ordinary people waited till life disclosed to them its secrets, but to the few, to the elect, the mysteries of life were revealed before the veil was drawn away.

OSCAR WILDE, *The Picture of Dorian Gray*

July 19th

1919 – Official peace celebrations took place throughout Britain. Virginia Woolf wrote in her diary: 'It was a melancholy thing to see the incurable soldiers ... with their backs turned to us, smoking cigarettes & waiting for the noise to be over. We were children to be amused ... '

———

For now that it was all over, truce signed, and the dead buried, he had, especially in the evening, these sudden thunderclaps of fear. He could not feel.

Mrs Dalloway

July 20th

1923 – Edward, Prince of Wales, drove through the streets of Dorchester with Thomas Hardy before lunching with him at Max Gate.

It was nearly ninety years ago. The British uniform of the period, with its immense epaulettes, queer cocked hat, breeches, gaiters, ponderous cartridge-box, buckled shoes, and what not, would look strange and barbarous now ... Soldiers were monumental objects then. A divinity still hedged kings here and there; and war was considered a glorious thing.

THOMAS HARDY, 'The Melancholy Hussar' from *The Melancholy Hussar and Other Stories*

July 21st

1933 – Graham Greene began 'with immense pleasure Graves's *Goodbye to All That* ... full of the right kind of anecdote, ones which set the creative instinct going'.

———

[The major] said: 'I was busy dying; but a company sergeant-major had got it through the head, and *he* was busy dying, too; and he did die. Well, as soon as ever the sergeant-major died, they took out that long gut, whatever you call the thing, the thing that unwinds – they say it's as long as a cricket pitch – and they put it into me, grafted it on somehow. Wonderful chaps these medicos! They supply spare parts as though one were a motor car ... Well, this sergeant-major seems to have been an abstemious man. The lining of the new gut is much better than my old one; so I'm celebrating it. I only wish I'd borrowed his kidneys, too.'

Goodbye to All That

July 22nd

1915 – Edward Thomas wrote to tell his friend Robert Frost that he had decided to enlist. He was killed by one of the last shells fired at the Battle of Arras as he stood up to light his pipe.

———

The cherry trees bend over and are shedding,
On the old road where all that passed are dead,
Their petals, strewing the grass as for a wedding
This early May morn when there is none to wed.

'The Cherry Trees' from
Poetry of the First World War

July 23rd

1917 – Siegfried Sassoon arrived at Craiglockhart War Hospital which specialised in neurasthenia; his stay 'brought Wilfred Owen into my life (for the last fifteen months of *his*)'.

———

Then I heard that Siegfried had been shot through the head ... but not killed. And he wrote me a verse-letter from a London hospital (which I cannot quote, though I should like to do so) beginning: 'I'd timed my death in action to the minute ... ' It is the most terrible of his war poems.

ROBERT GRAVES, *Goodbye to All That*

July 24th

1895 – Robert Graves was born in Wimbledon. His mother was of German descent. His father edited an Irish literary magazine and was a minor poet.

I called to Moodie, 'I've been hit.' Then I fell ... I wrote home to my mother: 'I am wounded, but am all right.' This was July 24th, my twenty-first birthday, and also the official date of my death. She got the letter two days after that written by the colonel; mine was dated 'July 23rd', because I had lost count of days; his, the 22nd. They could not decide whether my letter had been written just before I died and misdated, or whether I had died just after writing it. 'Died of wounds', however, seemed so much more circumstantial than 'killed' that ... they gave me up.

Goodbye to All That

July 25th

1926 – The Woolfs went to Dorchester to have tea with the Hardys. Thomas Hardy told Virginia he had seen her in her cradle. He said: 'Your father took my novel – *Far from the Madding Crowd*. We stood shoulder to shoulder against the British public about certain matters dealt with in that novel.'

She belonged to him: the certainties of that position were so well defined, and the reasonable probabilities of its issue so bounded, that she could not speculate on contingencies ... soon, or later – and that not very late – her husband would be home again. And then the days of their tenancy of the Upper Farm would be numbered.

Far from the Madding Crowd

Illustration from *Far from the Madding Crowd*

July 26th

1915 – Henry James became a British citizen as a declaration of loyalty to his adopted country and in protest against America's refusal to enter the war.

———

'He *has* done a lot of reading, and he says it opened his eyes. He says that a wave of disgust rolled over him. He talked about the "immeasurable misery" of wars, and asked me why nations don't tear to pieces the governments, the rulers that go in for them.'

Owen Wingrave from
The Turn of the Screw and Owen Wingrave

July 27th

2010 – The 'lost' tombstone of Robert Seymour, ill-fated original illustrator of *The Pickwick Papers*, went on permanent display at the Charles Dickens Museum. In conflict with Dickens over his images for the book, Seymour shot himself on 20 April 1836, and was buried, without religious rites, in the churchyard of St Mary Magdalene in Islington. The tombstone was consigned to the crypt and was 'lost' until re-discovered by a biographer of Seymour.

———

Illustration from *The Pickwick Papers*

_____

_____

_____

_____

_____

July 28th

1915 – William Noel Hodgson landed in Le Havre on his way to the trenches. He was killed on the first day of the Battle of the Somme. He was twenty-three.

> I, that on my familiar hill
>   Saw with uncomprehending eyes
> A hundred of Thy sunsets spill
>   Their fresh and sanguine sacrifice,
> Ere the sun swings his noonday sword
>   Must say goodbye to all of this;
> By all delights that I shall miss,
>   Help me to die, O Lord.

'Before Action' from *Poetry of the First World War*

July 29th

1913 – *The Times* published letters Charlotte Brontë had written to Constantin Heger after leaving Brussels in 1844. They somewhat damaged her image as an angelic martyr to the Victorian moral code.

And I'm sure poor Charlotte Brontë ... did *not* have any deliberate intention to stimulate sex feelings in the reader ... Wagner and Charlotte Brontë were both in the state where the strongest instincts have collapsed, and sex has become something slightly obscene, to be wallowed in, but despised. Mr Rochester's sex passion is not 'respectable' till Mr Rochester is burned, blinded and disfigured, and reduced to helpless dependence. Then, thoroughly humbled and humiliated, it may be merely admitted.

D. H. LAWRENCE

July 30th

1847 – Charles Dickens paid a call on Hans Christian Andersen who was visiting England for the first time. On a subsequent visit Dickens invited him to stay for two weeks at Gadshill. The 'bony bore' stayed for five weeks which 'seemed to the family AGES!' It is said that Andersen provided Dickens with the physical model for Uriah Heep.

One night as she lay in her cradle, a horrible toad hopped in through the window – one of the panes was broken. This big, ugly, slimy toad jumped right down on the table where Thumbelina was asleep under the red rose petal.

'Here's a perfect wife for my son!' the toad exclaimed.

'Thumbelina' from
Best Fairy Stories of Hans Christian Andersen

July 31st

1944 – Antoine de Saint-Exupéry took off on a reconnaissance mission from which he never returned.

I think he latched on to a flight of migrating birds to make his escape.

On the morning of his departure, he put his planet in good order. He carefully chimney-swept the active volcanoes. There were two active volcanoes which were very useful for cooking breakfast in the morning. There was also one extinct volcano, but, as he used to say, 'You never know!' and so he chimney-swept the extinct volcano too. If volcanoes are properly swept, they burn slowly and steadily, without erupting.

The Little Prince

August 1st

1862 – Birth of M. R. James in Kent. A distinguished medieval scholar, he became provost of King's College, Cambridge, and later of Eton College. He is known as the originator of the 'antiquarian ghost story' and set many of his macabre tales in Suffolk where he spent much of his childhood.

I can only call it a laugh: and if you can understand what I mean by a breathless, a lungless laugh, you have it: but I don't suppose you can. It came from below, and swerved away into the mist. That was enough. We bent over the wall. Paxton was there at the bottom.

You don't need to be told that he was dead ... His mouth was full of sand and stones, and his teeth and jaws were broken to bits.

'A Warning to the Curious' from
Complete Ghost Stories

August 2nd

1920 – Virginia Woolf wrote in her diary: 'Poor L. [Leonard], utterly driven for a month by Tolstoy and Morgan, confessed to feeling tired ... As a hobby, The Hogarth Press is clearly too lively & lusty to be carried on in this private way any longer.'

You know that you are one of the only living writers whom I can read with joy and perpetual astonishment and satisfaction, and the fact that you like my poems makes me proud and happy. Not only are you one of the only living writers whom I can read with delight but you are one of the only people whom I really enjoy talking to.

EDITH SITWELL in a letter to Virginia Woolf

August 3rd

1924 – Joseph Conrad died in Canterbury. He was interred in the Cathedral under a misspelt version of his original Polish name. His modest funeral took place during a cricket festival.

[If I could bring Conrad back to life] by grinding
Mr Eliot into a fine dry powder and sprinkling that
powder over Conrad's grave in Canterbury, [I would]
leave London early tomorrow morning with a
sausage-grinder.

ERNEST HEMINGWAY

August 4th

1875 – Hans Christian Andersen died at the age of
seventy from the far-reaching effects of having fallen
out of bed and been severely hurt in the spring of 1872.

They could see she was a real princess and no question about it, now that she had felt one pea all the way through twenty mattresses and twenty more feather beds. Nobody but a princess could be so delicate. So the prince made haste to marry her, because he knew he had found a real princess.

'The Princess and the Pea' from
Best Fairy Tales of Hans Christian Andersen

August 5th

1895 – Friedrich Engles died of throat cancer in London. Following cremation at Woking Crematorium, his ashes were scattered off Beachy Head.

The weapons with which the bourgeoisie felled feudalism to the ground are now turned against the bourgeoisie itself. But not only has the bourgeoisie forged the weapons that bring death to itself; it has also called into existence the men who are to wield those weapons – the modern working class – the proletarians.

Selected Writings of Karl Marx and Friedrich Engels

August 6th

1816 – Despite a grave deterioration in her health, Jane Austen finally completed 'The Elliots' to her satisfaction. After her death the book was published under the title *Persuasion*.

———

'The little Durands were there, I conclude,' said she, 'with their mouths open to catch the music, like unfledged sparrows ready to be fed. They never miss a concert.'

Persuasion

August 7th

1879 – Robert Louis Stevenson set sail on the first lap of his journey to California to marry Fanny van de Grift.

———

Stevenson's letters are most disappointing – I see that romantic surroundings are the worst surroundings possible for a romantic writer.

OSCAR WILDE

from *Persuasion*

August 8th

1912 – Leonard Woolf portrayed his mother as grotesquely over-dressed, addicted to small talk and peevish. Two days before the Woolfs' wedding Virginia mentioned in a letter that Mrs Woolf was outraged at being refused an invitation. She lived to be ninety-one and in old age was 'as spry as a weasel'.

There were the Bradshaws, whom she disliked. She must go up to Lady Bradshaw (in grey and silver, balancing like a sea-lion at the edge of its tank, barking for invitations, the typical successful man's wife), she must go up to Lady Bradshaw and say ...
    But Lady Bradshaw anticipated her.
    'We are shockingly late, dear Mrs Dalloway; we hardly dared to come in,' she said.

Mrs Dalloway

August 9th

1936 – Death of Arthur B. Reeve, American mystery writer who created Professor Craig Kennedy, sometimes called the American Sherlock Holmes.

Suddenly from the shrubbery across the road ... there came the crack of a gun, followed by a whir, a ping and a rip. It was a bullet that had passed through the top of the car, not two feet from where Craig was sitting ...

'Who sent me that billet-doux?' he muttered, glancing up at the hole drilled in the leather top.

'The Black Cross' from *Vintage Detective Stories*

August 10th

1912 – Virginia Stephen married writer Leonard Woolf. In 1937 she wrote, 'After twenty-five years can't bear to be separate.'

Mr Ramsay stumbling along a passage stretched his arms out one dark morning, but, Mrs Ramsay having died rather suddenly the night before, he stretched his arms out. They remained empty.

To the Lighthouse

August 11th

1879 – Frieda van Richthofen, cousin of the German flying ace Baron Mannfred von Richthofen (the Red Baron) and wife of D. H. Lawrence, was born on this day (and died on this day in 1956). She met Lawrence in 1912, left her first husband for him, and they were together till his death in 1930.

'So they won't be able to blow out my wanting you, nor the little glow there is between you and me. We'll be together next year. And though I'm frightened, I believe in your being with me. A man has to fend and fettle for the best, and then trust in something beyond himself. You can't insure against the future, except by really believing in the best bit of you, and in the power beyond it. So I believe in the little flame between us. For me now, it's the only thing in the world.'

Lady Chatterley's Lover

August 12th

1668 – Samuel Pepys attended a performance of *Macbeth* 'to our great content'. It was the seventh time he had seen the play.

Here's the smell of the blood still: all the perfumes of Arabia will not sweeten this little hand.

WILLIAM SHAKESPEARE, *Macbeth*

August 13th

1957 – Graham Greene planned a trip to Moscow, Leningrad and Vienna with his son Francis. A high spot was to be a visit to Tolstoy's estate at Yasnaya Polyana which even before Tolstoy's death had become a place of pilgrimage.

———

When he returned to the country in June, he went back to his ordinary occupations – husbandry, intercourse with the peasants and with his neighbours, management of his house and of his sister's and brother's affairs, which were entrusted to him, relations with his wife and relatives, cares about his baby, and a new hobby – beekeeping, which he took up with enthusiasm that spring – occupied all his time.

LEO TOLSTOY, *Anna Karenina*

August 14th

1937 – Cyril McNeile died in Sussex. Drawing on his experiences in the trenches during World War I he had begun writing short stories; as serving officers were not permitted to publish under their own names, Lord Northcliffe suggested he use the pen name 'Sapper'. His best known creation was Bulldog Drummond. Ian Fleming admitted that James Bond was: 'Sapper from the waist up and Micky Spillane below'.

We've both seen exactly what he's seen; we both know the facts just as well as he does. We're neither of us fools, and yet he can see the solution – and we can't.'

'The Horror at Staveley Grange' from
Vintage Detective Stories

August 15th

1858 – Edith Nesbit was born in Kennington. The decline of the family fortunes after the death of her father meant that her childhood was bohemenian and nomadic. Her first husband, Hubert Bland, was a notorious womaniser, but such was her forbearance that Edith allowed his illegitimate offspring to live in the household along with her own four children. She began writing at an early age.

You will think that they ought to have been very happy. And so they were, but they did not know *how* happy till the pretty life in the Red Villa was over and done with, and they had to live a very different life indeed.

The dreadful change came quite suddenly.

The Railway Children

August 16th

1917 – Geoffrey Studdert Kennedy, poet and Anglican priest, was commended for 'conspicuous bravery' in the *London Gazette*. He was nicknamed Woodbine Willie for giving cigarettes along with spiritual aid to the injured and dying soldiers. James Joyce mentions him in *Finnegans Wake*: ' ... tsingirillies' zyngarettes, while Woodbine Willie, so popiular with the poppy-rossies, blued the air'.

They gave me this name like their nature,
Compacted of laughter and tears,
A sweet that was born of the bitter,
A joke that was torn from the years

Of their travail and torture, Christ's fools,
Atoning my sins with their blood,
Who grinned in their agony sharing
The glorious madness of God.

Their name! Let me hear it -- the symbol
Of unpaid – unpayable debt,
For the men to whom I owed God's Peace,
I put off with a cigarette.

'Woodbine Willie' from
Poetry of the First World War

Illustration from *Through the Looking-Glass*

August 17th

1935 – Death of Charlotte Perkins Gilman. A passionate feminist, she had approached marriage with some misgivings, and when to cure her severe post-natal depression she was advised 'never touch pen, brush or pencil as long as you live', she began her descent into madness.

———

Then I peeled off all the paper I could reach standing on the floor. It sticks horribly and the pattern just enjoys it! All those strangled heads and bulbous eyes and waddling fungus growths just shriek with derision!

'The Yellow Wallpaper' from
Classic Tales of the Macabre

August 18th

1945 – Graham Greene was disappointed in Somerset Maugham: 'There is such immense talent, couldn't he ... have tried for something a little more difficult ... taken a few risks ... ?'

———

He was bound hand and foot and couldn't move ... he opened his eyes and saw Mrs Baines was there, her grey untidy hair in threads over his face, her black hat askew. A loose hairpin fell on the pillow and one musty thread brushed his mouth. 'Where are they?' she whispered. 'Where are they?'

GRAHAM GREENE, 'The Fallen Idol' from
The Third Man and Other Stories

August 19th

1886 – Joseph Conrad was granted British nationality.

I have not forgotten ... the first English ship on whose side I ever laid my hand! ... A few strokes brought us alongside, and it was then that, for the very first time in my life, I heard myself addressed in English – the speech of my secret choice, of my future, of long friendships, of the deepest affections, of hours of toil and hours of ease, and of solitary hours, too, of books read, of thoughts pursued, of remembered emotions – of my very dreams!

A Personal Record

August 20th

1973 – In reviewing *The Honorary Consul*, Auberon Waugh wrote: 'Graham Greene is an enormous brooding presence over the English novel ... One can only gasp and cross oneself and vow never to compare another novelist to him again.'

———

It was as if he were dead and were remembering the effect of a good confession, the words of absolution: but being dead it was a memory only – he couldn't experience contrition – the ribs of his body were like steel bands which held him down to eternal un-repentance.

Brighton Rock

August 21st

1915 – At the request of Henry James, W. B. Yeats sent off a poem, 'A Reason for Keeping Silent', to Edith Wharton for her to include in an anthology to raise money for Belgian refugees. The title was later changed.

———

I think it better that in times like these
A poet's mouth be silent, for in truth
We have no gift to set a statesman right;

He has had enough of meddling who can please
A young girl in the indolence of her youth,
Or an old man upon a winter's night.

'On being asked for a War Poem' from
Collected Poems of W. B. Yeats

August 22nd

1962 – An attempt was made to assassinate Charles
de Gaulle in Paris. The incident provided Frederick
Forsyth with material for his novel *The Day of the
Jackal*.

The Jackal raised the rifle and squinted down into the
forecourt. He picked the war veteran nearest to him,
the man who would be the first to get his medal ... In
a few minutes, facing this man, about one foot taller,
would be another face, proud, arrogant, topped by a
khaki *képi* adorned with two gold stars on the front.

The Day of the Jackal

August 23rd

1914 – Alan Seeger, a young American poet who had been a classmate of T. S. Eliot's at Harvard, joined the French Foreign Legion so that he could fight for the Allies when war broke out. He was killed in action on 4 July 1916.

    I have a rendezvous with Death
At some disputed barricade,
When spring comes back with rustling shade
And apple-blossoms fill the air –
I have a rendezvous with Death
When spring brings back blue days and fair.

'Rendezvous' from
Poetry of the First World War

August 24th

1872 – Max Beerbohm, 'the Incomparable Max', was born in London, the son of a Lithuanian grain merchant. 'It always makes me cross,' wrote Vita Sackville West, 'when Max is called "The Incomparable Max". He is not incomparable at all ... He is a shallow, affected, self-conscious fribble – so there.'

'Know, too, Miss Dobson, that in the Peerage of France I am Duc d'Étretat et de la Roche Guillaume. Louis Napoleon gave the title to my father for not cutting him in the Bois.'

Zuleika Dobson

August 25th

1938 – Frederick Forsyth was born in Kent. Before becoming a full-time writer, he was a jet-fighter pilot with the RAF, a journalist with Reuters and a diplomatic correspondent and documentary maker with the BBC.

The Baroness, on her knees amid the debris, looked up with wide staring eyes. Around her lay a series of slim steel tubes, from each of which the hessian caps that closed the open ends had been removed. From one emerged the end of a telescopic sight, from another the snout of the silencer. She held something in her hands, something she had been gazing at in horror when he entered. It was the barrel and breech of the gun.

The Day of the Jackal

August 26th

1875 – John Buchan, destined to become 1st Baron Tweedsmuir, was born in Perth in Scotland. During a distinguished career in national and international politics, he managed a prodigious output of novels, poetry and biographies – and even dabbled in publishing.

He was turbaned and rode like one possessed, and against the snow I caught the dark sheen of emerald. As he rode it seemed that the fleeing Turks were stricken still, and sank by the roadside with eyes strained after his unheeding figure . . .

Then I knew that the prophecy had been true, and that their prophet had not failed them. The long-looked-for revelation had come. Greenmantle had appeared at last to an awaiting people.

Greenmantle

August 27th

1897 – Virginia Woolf recorded simply: 'Rained. We went out somewhere, I think, but I quite forget.'

———

I have heard a good deal about the wonders of Mrs Woolf's style. She sometimes discovers a truly brilliant simile. She often chooses her adjectives and adverbs with beautiful felicity. But there is more in style than this. The form of her sentences is rather tryingly monotonous, and the distance between her nominatives and her verbs is steadily increasing.

ARNOLD BENNETT

August 28th

1844 – Karl Marx met German sociologist Friedrich Engels in Paris at the Café de la Régence, and they began a lifelong friendship.

———

'All I know is that I am not a Marxist.'

KARL MARX quoted by Friedrich Engels

August 29th

1918 – Siegfried Sassoon spent the day rescuing and reading a volume of Thomas Hardy. 'Glorious Hardy,' he wrote the following day. 'I will go and pour ointment on his feet someday, when they let me out of this charming hospital.'

———

Shortly after his birthday [in 1919] he received a charming volume of holograph poems, beautifully bound, from some forty or fifty living poets ... This 'Poets' Tribute' had been arranged by his friend Siegfried Sassoon, who brought the gift and placed it in Hardy's hand.

FLORENCE HARDY

August 30th

1854 – Bernard Capes was born into a large and bookish family in London and became a prolific and successful novelist. He died in the flu epidemic of 1918.

He fetched out his knife indeed, and, hunting over the surface of the thing, found a blister in the paint, cut into it, seized an edge between thumb and finger, and, flaying away a long strip, uttered a loud, jubilant exclamation.

'The Mask' from *Spinechillers*

Illustration from *A Shropshire Lad*

August 31st

1920 – Virginia Woolf 'sat in the meadow [at Rodmell] & watched Squire and Sassoon play cricket'. J. C. Squire was a poet, writer and historian and a seriously influential literary editor of the post-World War I period.

———

God heard the embattled nations sing and shout,
'Gott strafe England!' and, 'God save the King!'
God this, God that, and God the other thing –
'Good God!' said God, 'I've got my work cut out.'

J. C. SQUIRE, 'The Dilemma' from
Poetry of the First World War

September 1st

1967 – Siegfried Sassoon died one week before his eighty-first birthday of stomach cancer and is buried at St Andrew's Church, Mells, Somerset, close to Ronald Knox. Sassoon had converted to Roman Catholicism before his death.

He told me that he had just been down to the Formby links and thrown his Military Cross into the sea ... Much against my will, I had to appear in the role of a patriot distressed by the mental collapse of a brother-in-arms – a collapse directly due to his magnificent exploits in the trenches. I mentioned Siegfried's 'hallucinations' of corpses strewn along Piccadilly. The irony of having to argue to these mad old men that Siegfried was not sane!

ROBERT GRAVES, *Goodbye to All That*

September 2nd

1930 – The Woolfs' furnishings at Rodmell were at first very modest. Virginia wrote: 'For years I never had a … comfortable bed, or a chair that did not want stuffing.'

All the colours in the room had over-flown their banks. The precise brushstroke was swollen and lopsided; cupboards and chairs melted their brown masses into one huge obscurity. The height from floor to ceiling was hung with vast curtains of shaking darkness. The looking-glass was pale as the mouth of a cave shadowed by hanging creepers.

The Waves

September 3rd

1918 – Alec de Candole, World War I poet, was killed in action in the last weeks of the war. He was twenty-one.

And if a bullet in the midst of strife
Should still the pulse of this unquiet life
'Twere well: be death an everlasting rest,
I oft could yearn for it, by cares opprest; …
Only the fierce and rending agony,
The torment of the flesh about to die.
Affrights my soul; but that shall pass anon,

And death's repose or strife be found, that gone;
Only with that last earthly ill to cope
God grant me strength, and I go forth with hope.

'And if a bullet' from *Poetry of the First World War*

September 4th

1948 – Raymond Chandler wrote: 'I did not invent
the hard-boiled murder story and I have never made
any secret of my opinion that Hammett deserves most
or all of the credit.'

———

She removed her clothes swiftly, without fumbling,
letting them fall down on the floor around her feet.
When she was naked she stepped back from her
clothing and stood looking at him. In her mien was
pride without defiance or embarrassment.

He put his pistols on the toilet-seat and, facing
the door, went down on one knee in front of her
garments. He picked up each piece and examined it
with fingers as well as eyes. He did not find the
thousand-dollar bill. When he had finished he stood
up holding her clothes out in his hands to her.
'Thanks,' he said. 'Now I know.'

DASHIELL HAMMETT, *The Maltese Falcon*

September 5th

1926 – Virginia Woolf wrote in her diary of her childlessness: 'a little more self-control on my part, & we might have had a boy of twelve, a girl of ten; this always makes me wretched in the early hours.'

———

James Ramsay, sitting on the floor cutting out pictures from the illustrated catalogue of the Army and Navy Stores, endowed the picture of a refrigerator as his mother spoke with heavenly bliss. It was fringed with joy.

To the Lighthouse

September 6th

1939 – Arthur Rackham died of cancer at seventy-one, having presided over the golden age of book illustration.

———

September 7th

1847 – After two years, two months and two days living at Walden Pond, Henry David Thoreau resumed life in the outside world. He described himself as having been born in the 'nick of time', during the flowering of America.

In any weather, at any hour of the day or night, I have been anxious to improve the nick of time, and notch it on my stick too; to stand on the meeting of two eternities, the past and future, which is precisely the present moment; to toe that line.

Walden

September 8th

1886 – Siegfried Sassoon, English poet, writer and soldier, was born in Kent. Decorated for bravery on the Western Front, he became one of the leading poets of the First World War.

———

Siegfried distinguished himself by taking, single-handed, a battalion frontage which the Royal Irish Regiment had failed to take the day before. He went over with bombs in daylight, under covering fire from a couple of rifles, and scared away the occupants. A pointless feat, since instead of signalling for reinforcements, he sat down in the German trench and began reading a book of poems which he had brought with him.

Goodbye to All That

September 9th

1828 – Birth of Leo Tolstoy on the family estate of Yasnaya Polyana. His parents were distinguished members of the Russian nobility.

———

Tolstoy renounced wealth, fame and privilege; he abjured violence in all its forms and was ready to suffer for doing so; but it is not easy to believe that he abjured the principle of coercion, or at least the *desire* to coerce others ... The distinction that really matters is not between violence and non-violence, but between having and not having the appetite for power.

GEORGE ORWELL

September 10th

1797 – Mary Wollstonecraft died of puerperol fever after giving birth to a daughter who on her marriage would become Mary Shelley. A fierce feminist, 'a hyena in petticoats', she inspired Virginia Woolf to write: 'We hear her voice and trace her influence even now among the living.'

But I discovered no trace of him, and was beginning to conjecture that some fortunate chance had intervened to prevent the execution of his menaces, when suddenly I heard a shrill and dreadful scream. It came from the room into which Elizabeth had retired. As I heard it, the whole truth rushed into my mind, my arms dropped, the motion of every muscle and fibre was suspended; I could feel the blood trickling in my veins and tingling in the extremities of my limbs. This state lasted but for an instant; the scream was repeated, and I rushed into the room.

MARY SHELLEY, Frankenstein

September 11th

1885 – D. H. Lawrence was born into the family of a barely literate miner and his schoolteacher wife in a coal-mining community in Nottinghamshire.

———

Mr Lawrence looked like a plaster gnome on a stone toadstool in some suburban garden ... He had a rather matted, dank appearance. He looked as if he had just returned from spending an uncomfortable night in a very dark cave, hiding, perhaps, in the darkness, from something which, at the same time, he on his side was hunting. His hair, which had been very red, was now dimmed by illness, as though dust, or ash, had quenched that flame. It hung down, at moments, into his bright and eager eyes, hindering him from seeing anything.

EDITH SITWELL

September 12th

1898 – Arnold Bennett wrote in his journal: 'I have decided very seriously to take up fiction for a livelihood ... I propose to give myself to writing the sort of fiction that sells itself.'

———

Of Dickens, I know nothing. About a year ago, from idle curiosity, I picked up *The Old Curiosity Shop*, & of all the rotten vulgar un-literary writing ... ! Worse than George Eliot's. If a novelist can't *write* where *is* the beggar?

ARNOLD BENNETT

September 13th

1919 – Ironically in view of her bouts of depression, Virginia Woolf wrote in her diary: 'I think perhaps nine people out of ten never get a day in the year of such happiness as I have almost constantly.'

He had never felt so happy in the whole of his life! Without a word they made it up. They walked down to the lake. He had twenty minutes of perfect happiness ... They sat on the ground and talked – he and Clarissa. They went in and out of each other's minds without any effort. And then in a second it was over.

Mrs Dalloway

September 14th

1851 – James Fenimore Cooper died in Cooperstown, New York. One of America's most distinguished early novelists, his reputation rests largely on the 'Leatherstocking Tales' featuring Hawkeye, the frontier scout.

———

The lightning is not quicker than was the flame from the rifle of Hawkeye; the limbs of the victim trembled and contracted, the head fell to the bosom, and the body parted the foaming waters like lead, when the element closed above it, in its ceaseless velocity, and every vestige of the unhappy Huron was lost for ever.

The Last of the Mohicans

September 15th

1789 – James Fenimore Cooper was born in Burlington, New Jersey. Expelled from Yale, he had gone to sea as a young man and did not become a novelist until he was in his thirties. His later years were much disturbed by literary and newspaper controversies and litigation.

———

The form of the Huron trembled in every fibre, and he raised his arm on high, but dropped it again with a bewildered air, like one who doubted ... but just then a piercing cry was heard above them, and Uncas appeared, leaping frantically, from a fearful height, upon the ledge. Magua recoiled a step; and one of his assistants, profiting by the chance, sheathed his own knife in the bosom of Cora.

The Last of the Mohicans

September 16th

1883 – T. E. Hulme, modernist poet and critic, was born in Staffordshire. He was killed by a shell on the Western Front in 1917.

Over the flat slope of St Eloi
A wide wall of sandbags.
Night,
In the silence desultory men
Pottering over small fires, cleaning their mess-tins:
To and fro, from the lines,
Men walk as on Piccadilly,
Making paths in the dark,
Through scattered dead horses,
Over a dead Belgian's belly.

'Trenches: St Eloi'
from *Poetry of the First World War*

September 17th

1917 – Ivor Gurney, composer and poet, wrote to his friend Marion Scott: 'Being gassed (mildly) with the new gas is no worse than catarrh or a bad cold.'

Who died on the wires, and hung there, one of two –
Who for his hours of life had chattered through
Infinite lovely chatter of Bucks accent ...

'The Silent One' from *Poetry of the First World War*

September 18th

1923 – Virginia Woolf recorded: 'Talking of Proust and [D. H.] Lawrence, Morgan said he'd prefer to be Lawrence but much rather would be himself.'

'And I am alive now,' he went on, 'because I had neither parents nor relatives nor friends, so that, when the first night came, I could run through the woods, and climb the rocks, and plunge into the water, until I had accomplished my desire!'

E. M. FORSTER, 'The Story of a Panic' from
The Machine Stops and Other Stories

Illustration from *The Arabian Nights*

September 19th

1867 – Arthur Rackham, accomplished and widely celebrated book illustrator, was born in Lewisham. Many of the most iconic children's books of the early twentieth century, especially collections of famous fairy stories, owe a measure of their success to his genius.

Illustration from *The Enchanted World*

September 20th

1882 – After unhappy years at school in England, Rudyard Kipling sailed for his beloved India, the place of his birth in 1865.

The bright colours of the bazaars dazzle one's eyes. The jaded, second-rate Anglo-Indians are in exquisite incongruity with their surroundings. The mere lack of style of the story-teller gives an old journalistic realism to what he tells us. From the point of view of life, he is a reporter who knows vulgarity better than anyone has ever known it. Dickens knew its clothes and its comedy. Mr Kipling knows its essence and its seriousness. He is our first authority on the second-rate and has seen marvellous things through the keyholes, and his backgrounds are real works of art.

OSCAR WILDE

September 21st

1832 – Death of Sir Walter Scott – 'It was so quiet a day,' wrote Lockhart, 'that the sound he best loved, the gentle ripple of the Tweed over its pebbles, was distinctly audible as we knelt round the bed and his eldest son kissed and closed his eyes.'

When the helmet was removed, the well-formed yet sunburnt features of a young man of twenty-five were seen, amidst a profusion of short fair hair. His countenance was as pale as death and marked in one or two places with streaks of blood ... The name of Ivanhoe was no sooner pronounced than it flew from mouth to mouth, with all the celerity with which eagerness could convey and curiosity receive it.

Ivanhoe

September 22nd

1916 – Edward Wyndham 'Bim' Tennant was killed at the Battle of the Somme. He was nineteen.

I dropp'd here three weeks ago, yes – I know,
And it's bitter cold at night, since the fight –
I could tell you if I chose ...

'The Mad Soldier' from *Poetry of the First World War*

September 23rd

1889 – Death of Wilkie Collins at sixty-five following a stroke. He had led a complicated life, never having married but having established long-term liaisons with two separate households.

———

A stone, set like a pommel, in the end of the dagger's handle, flashed in the torchlight, as he turned on me, like a gleam of fire. The dying Indian sank to his knees, pointed to the dagger in Herncastle's hand, and said, in his native language: 'The Moonstone will have its vengeance yet on you and yours!' He spoke those words, and fell dead on the floor.

The Moonstone

Illustration from *David Copperfield*

September 24th

1848 – Branwell Brontë, the 'failure of the family', died of consumption.

————

I have heard, from one who attended Branwell in his last illness, that he resolved on standing up to die. He had repeatedly said that as long as there was life there was strength of will to do what it chose; and when the last agony came on, he insisted on assuming the position just mentioned. I have previously stated, that when his fatal attack came on, his pockets were found filled with old letters from the woman to whom he was attached.

ELIZABETH GASKELL

September 25th

1928 – Arnold Bennett finished reading *Lady Chatterley's Lover*: 'It is *foncièrement* indecent, but not pornographic. Some of it is very good, and some awful in dryness. Generally speaking the lechery scenes are the best.'

————

She felt the glide of his cheek on her thighs and belly ... and the close brushing of his moustache and his soft thick hair, and her knees began to quiver. Far down in her she felt a new stirring, a new nakedness emerging.

And she was half afraid. Half she wished he would not caress her so. He was encompassing her some-how. Yet she was waiting, waiting.

D. H. LAWRENCE, *Lady Chatterley's Lover*

September 26th

1921 – T. S. Eliot left Monks House after a weekend with the Woolfs. Virginia reported that the visit passed off successfully, '& yet I am disappointed to find that I am no longer afraid of him'.

———

I could wish that poor dear Tom had more spunk in him, less need to let drop by drop of his agonised perplexities fall ever so finely through pure cambric. One waits, one sympathises, but it is dreary work ,,,

VIRGINIA WOOLF

Illustration from *Three Men in a Boat*

September 27th

1893 – E. W. Hornung married Conan Doyle's sister Constance. Their only child was a son who was killed at the Second Battle of Ypres on 6 July 1915. His creation was the gentleman burglar, A. J. Raffles, and he inscribed his first volume of tales, *The Amateur Cracksman*, 'To A. C. D. this sincere form of flattery', in recognition of Doyle's influence and encouragement.

———

They were searching the shrubberies between the drive and the road; a policeman's lantern kept flashing in and out among the laurels, while a young man in evening clothes directed him from the gravel sweep. It was this young man whom I must dodge, but at my first step on the gravel he wheeled round, and it was Raffles himself.

'Out of Paradise' from *Vintage Detective Stories*

September 28th

1891 – Herman Melville died in New York City. The fictionalised accounts of his youthful travels *Typee* and *Omoo* were the most popular of his books during his lifetime but his great American epic *Moby-Dick* secured him a place in literary history.

———

But at last, some three points off the weather bow, Ahab descried the spout again, and instantly from the three mast-heads three shrieks went up as if the tongues of fire had voiced it.

'Forehead to forehead I meet thee, this third time, Moby-Dick!'

Moby-Dick

September 29th

1810 – Elizabeth Gaskell was born in Chelsea but was sent to live with her aunt in Cheshire when her mother died thirteen months later. She grew up with a highly developed social conscience, married a Unitarian minister and settled in Manchester. Her novels are set in a world being changed for ever by the Industrial Revolution.

'Nothing like the act of eating for equalising men. Dying is nothing to it. The philosopher dies sententiously – the pharisee ostentatiously – the simple-hearted humbly – the poor idiot blindly, as the sparrow falls to the ground; the philosopher and idiot, publican and pharisee, all eat after the same fashion – given an equally good digestion.'

North and South

September 30th

1832 – Charlotte Riddell, who became one of the most popular and influential writers of the Victorian period, was born in Carrickfergus in Ireland. She was also part owner and editor of the *St James's Magazine*, a prestigious publication in the 1860s.

———

The horror of the silent house grew and grew upon him. He could hear the beating of his own heart in the dead quietude which reigned from garret to cellar.

'The Old House in Vauxhall Walk'
from *Spinechillers*

Illustration from *Hard Times*

October 1st

1918 – Wilfred Owen, having returned to the Front after his release from Craiglockhart War Hospital in Edinburgh, where he had been inspired by fellow poet Siegfried Sassoon, led units of the Second Manchesters into action at Joncourt.

Red lips are not so red
As the stained stones kissed by the English dead.

'Greater Love' from *Poetry of the First World War*

October 2nd

1904 – At 10.20 a.m. Graham Greene was born in Berkhampsted School in Hertfordshire where his father was a housemaster. He weighed in at 7¼ lbs.

He looked at the mousy skull, the bony body and the shabby dress, and shuddered – involuntarily ... remembering the room at home, the frightening weekly exercise of his parents which he watched from his single bed.

Brighton Rock

October 3rd

1928 – Arnold Bennett and H. G. Wells played tennis in Cadogen Square.

Harder ... pulled the trigger. Franting collapsed, with the upper half of his body somehow balanced on the edge of the billiard-table. He was dead. The report echoed in Harder's ear like the sound of a violin string loudly twanged by a finger. He saw a little reddish hole in Franting's bronzed right temple.

ARNOLD BENNETT, 'Murder' from *Vintage Detective Stories*

October 4th

1849 – Edgar Allan Poe died having been found on the previous day in the streets of Baltimore 'in great distress and in need of immediate assistance'.

I endeavoured to shriek; and my lips and my parched tongue moved convulsively together in the attempt – but no voice issued from the cavernous lungs, which, oppressed as if by the weight of some incumbent mountain, gasped and palpitated, with the heart, at every elaborate and struggling inspiration.

'The Premature Burial' from
Tales of Mystery and Imagination

Illustration from *Cider with Rosie*

October 5th

1915 – A critic described D. H. Lawrence's novel *The Rainbow* as 'windy, tedious, boring and nauseating'. In November over a thousand copies were seized by the police and subsequently destroyed.

———

Yet she flashed with excitement. In his dark, subterranean, male soul, he was kneeling before her, darkly exposing himself. She quivered, the dark flame ran over her. He was waiting at her feet. He was helpless, at her mercy. She could take or reject. If she rejected him, something would die in him. For him it was life or death. And yet, all must be kept so dark, the consciousness must admit nothing.

The Rainbow

October 6th

1868 – Charles Dickens embarked upon a series of 'farewell lectures'; he managed seventy-five in the provinces and twelve in London but when he collapsed in April 1869 the rest of the tour was cancelled.

———

Of Dickens's style it is impossible to speak in praise. It is jerky, ungrammatical, and created by himself in defiance of rules ... To readers who have taught themselves to regard language, it must therefore be

Illustration from *A Christmas Carol*

unpleasant. But the critic is driven to feel the weakness of his criticism when he acknowledges to himself – as he is compelled in all honesty to do – that with the language, such as it is, the writer has satisfied the great mass of the readers of his country.

ANTHONY TROLLOPE

October 7th

1946 – Raymond Chandler observed: 'A good title is the title of a successful book. *The Maltese Falcon* is [a good title] because it has rhyme and rhythm and makes the mind ask questions.'

————

She twisted convulsively around in his arms and caught at one of his hands with both of hers. He pulled his hand away quickly and looked at it. Across its back was a thin red scratch an inch and a half or more in length.

'What the hell?' he growled and examined her hands. Her left hand was empty. In her right hand, when he forced it open, lay a three-inch jade-headed steel bouquet-pin. 'What the hell?' he growled again and held the pin up in front of her eyes.

DASHIELL HAMMETT, *The Maltese Falcon*

Illustration from *Zuleika Dobson*

October 8th

1916 – Leslie Coulson, journalist and poet, died of wounds on the Western Front aged twenty-seven.

> Where war has left its wake of whitened bone,
> Soft stems of summer grass shall wave again,
> And all the blood that war has ever strewn
> > Is but a passing stain.

'War' from *Poetry of the First World War*

October 9th

1914 – Virginia Woolf wrote 'the last words of the last page of Mrs Dalloway'.

'I will come up,' said Peter, but he sat on for a moment. What is this terror? what is this ecstasy? he thought to himself. What is it that fills me with extraordinary excitement?

It is Clarissa, he said.

For there she was.

Mrs Dalloway

October 10th

1918 – Wilfrid Owen wrote: 'The boy by my side, shot through the head, lay on top of me, soaking my shoulder, for half an hour.' Owen himself was killed on 4 November.

... It is a great life. I am more oblivious than alas! yourself, dear Mother, of the ghastly glimmering of the guns outside, & the hollow crashing of the shells.

There is no danger down here, or if any, it will be well over before you read these lines.

I hope you are warm as I am; as serene in your room as I am here ... Of this I am certain you could not be visited by a band of friends half so fine as surround me here.

Ever Wilfred x

Last letter to his mother

October 11th

1943 – In his diary Chips Channon wrote: 'I sometimes see a dreary Alfred Douglasish old age. In fact, I am haunted by that sad, solitary leftover, eking out his existence surrounded by his few remaining possessions. How clumsily he must have arranged his life. He is a lesson to one.'

'The people who have adored me – there have not been very many, but there have been some – have always insisted on living on, long after I had ceased to care for them, or they to care for me.'

OSCAR WILDE, *The Picture of Dorian Gray*

October 12th

1912 – American music critic James Huneker visited Joseph Conrad and recalled 'a man of the world, neither sailor nor novelist, just a simple-mannered gentleman ... whose ways were French, Polish, anything but "literary", bluff or English.'

'I could never, somehow, imagine him either younger or older – don't you know. There was a sense of physical power about that man too. And perhaps that was the secret of that something peculiar in his person which struck everybody who came in contact with him. He looked indestructible by any ordinary means that put an end to the rest of us. His deliberate, stately courtesy of manner was full of significance. It was as though he were certain of having plenty of time for everything.'

JOSEPH CONRAD, 'The End of the Tether' from *Heart of Darkness and Other Stories*

October 13th

1874 – Joseph Conrad, aged sixteen, arrived in Marseilles from Kraków to begin his career at sea in accordance with his uncle's wishes.

———

I remember my youth and the feeling that will never come back any more – the feeling that I could last for ever, outlast the sea, the earth, and all men; the deceitful feeling that lures us on to joys, to perils, to love, to vain effort – to death; the triumphant conviction of strength, the heat of life in the handful of dust, the glow in the heart that with every year grows dim, grows cold, grows small, and expires – and expires, too soon, too soon – before life itself.

'Youth' from *The Heart of Darkness and Other Stories*

October 14th

1856 – Violet Paget was born in France. Remembered primarily for her supernatural fiction which she wrote under her pseudonym Vernon Lee and for her work on aesthetics, she was a passionate feminist and always dressed *à la garçonne*.

———

I heard the voice swelling, swelling, rending asunder that downy veil which wrapped it, leaping forth clear, resplendent, like the sharp and glittering blade of a knife that seemed to enter deep into my breast. Then, once more, a wail, a death-groan, and that dreadful noise, that hideous gurgle of breath strangled by a rush of blood. And then a long shake, acute, brilliant, triumphant.

'A Wicked Voice' from *Spinechillers*

October 15th

1897 – Joseph Conrad met Stephen Crane. Crane was born in New Jersey in 1871, the son of a Methodist minister. He worked as a journalist in New York and travelled as a newspaper correspondent to Mexico, Cuba and Greece. In 1897 he settled in England. His small body of work, notably *The Red Badge of Courage*, set him in the forefront of modern American fiction. He died of consumption in Germany in 1900 at the age of twenty-eight.

———

He knew little of literature, either of his own country or of any other, but he was himself a wonderful artist in words whenever he took a pen into his hand.

JOSEPH CONRAD
Introduction to *The Red Badge of Courage*

October 16th

1854 – Oscar Wilde was born in Dublin, the son of celebrated Irish intellectuals. His father was an internationally famous eye surgeon, whose reputation survived his many sexual exploits; his mother was talented and eccentric and wrote for a revolutionary newspaper under the *nom de plume* 'Speranza'.

———

If you wish for reputation and fame in the world and success during your lifetime, you are right to take every opportunity of advertising yourself. You remember the Latin saying, 'Fame springs from one's own house.'

OSCAR WILDE

October 17th

1896 – Following the critical outcry following the publication of *Jude the Obscure*, Hardy wrote that he had reached 'the end of prose'.

———

What has happened to Thomas Hardy? ... I am shocked, appalled by this story! ... It is the handling of it that is the horror of it ... I do not believe that there is a newspaper in England or America that would print this story of Thomas Hardy's as it stands in the book. Aside from its immorality there is a coarseness which is beyond belief ... When I finished the story I opened the windows and let in the fresh air, and I turned to my bookshelves and I said: 'Thank God for Kipling and Stevenson, Barrie and Mrs Humphry Ward. Here are four great writers who have never trailed their talents in the dirt.'

JEANETTE GILDER, *New York World*

October 18th

1924 – Charlotte Mew visited Thomas Hardy's second wife Florence, who was in a nursing home recovering from surgery. Charlotte, whose work spanned the divide between Victorian poetry and modernism, affected the dress of a dandy and would have cut a flamboyant figure on the ward.

———

Seventeen years ago you said
Something that sounded like Goodbye:
And everybody thinks that you are dead
    But I ...

CHARLOTTE MEW, 'A Quoi Bon Dire'

October 19th

1745 – Jonathan Swift died in Dublin and is buried in St Patrick's Cathedral, 'where fierce indignation can no longer injure the heart'.

———

He had been eight years upon a project for extracting sunbeams out of cucumbers, which were to be put into vials hermetically sealed, and let out to warm the air in raw, inclement summers.

Gulliver's Travels

October 20th

1890 – Sir Richard Burton died in Trieste. His wife Isabel persuaded a priest to perform the last rites. The couple are buried in a tomb in the shape of a Bedouin tent in Mortlake.

———

This book is indeed a legacy which I bequeath to my fellow-countrymen in their hour of need ... We may, perhaps, find it hard to restore to England those pristine virtues, that tone and temper, which made her what she is; but at any rate we (myself and a host of others) can offer her the means of dispelling her ignorance concerning the Eastern races with whom she is continually in contact.

Preface to *The Arabian Nights*

Illustration from *Gulliver's Travels*

October 21st

1912 – Death of Robert Barr, a writer who parodied Sherlock Holmes but was described by Conan Doyle as 'a volcanic Anglo- or rather Scot-American, with a violent manner, a wealth of strong adjectives, and one of the kindest natures underneath it all'.

I have ever considered the English nihilist the most dangerous of this fraternity, for he is cool-headed and not carried away by his own enthusiasm, and consequently rarely carried away by his own police.

'In the Grip of the Green Demon' from
Vintage Detective Stories

October 22nd

1942 – Raymond Chandler wrote: 'I hope the day will come when I won't have to ride around on Hammett ... like an organ grinder's monkey. Hammett is all right. I give him everything. There were a lot of things he could not do, but what he did he did superbly.'

Mr Joel Cairo was a small-boned dark man of medium height. His hair was black and smooth and very glossy. His features were Levantine. A square-cut ruby, its sides paralleled by four baguette diamonds, gleamed against the deep green of his cravat. His black coat, cut tight to narrow shoulders, flared a little over slightly plump hips. His trousers fitted his round legs more snugly than was the current fashion. The uppers of his patent-leather shoes were hidden by fawn spats. He held a black derby hat in a chamois-gloved hand and came towards Spade with short, mincing, bobbing steps. The fragrance of *chypre* came with him.

DASHIELL HAMMETT, *The Maltese Falcon*

Illustration from *Limericks*

October 23rd

1922 – A. E. Housman urged his publisher not to put an erratum slip in his *Last Poems*, because 'the blunder will probably enhance the first edition in the eyes of bibliophiles, an idiotic class'.

———

> Now, of my threescore years and ten,
> Twenty will not come again,
> And take from seventy springs a score,
> It only leaves me fifty more.
>
> And since to look at things in bloom
> Fifty springs are little room,
> About the woodlands I will go
> To see the cherry hung with snow ...

A Shropshire Lad

October 24th

1924 – In Mexico City, D. H. Lawrence wrote to Somerset Maugham: 'I feel that two such literary Englishmen as you and I ought not to pass as ships in the night, with a piece of wide sea in between. Would you like to come to lunch at this little place? If so you might ring up, or leave a message.' Maugham declined by telegram, pleading pressure of work.

Damn his eyes and his work ... a narrow-gutted 'artist' with a stutter ... no loss: a bit sour and full of nerves and fidgets lest he shouldn't produce a Maughnum opus with a Mexican background for Christmas. As if he could fail!

D. H. LAWRENCE

October 25th

1923 – D. H. Lawrence said of Katherine Mansfield as a writer: 'Poor Katherine, she is delicate and touching – But not Great! Why say great?'

Miriam shyly and rather bitterly produced her exercise-book. Every week she wrote for him a sort of diary of her inner life, in her own French ... He would read it now; she felt as if her soul's history were going to be desecrated by him in his present mood. He sat beside her. She watched his hand, firm and warm, rigorously scoring her work. He was reading only the French, ignoring her soul that was there.

D. H. LAWRENCE, *Sons and Lovers*

October 26th

1932 – Carl Jung sent his article on *Ulysses* to James Joyce. He said, 'Your book has given me no end of trouble ... you may gather from my article what *Ulysses* has done to a supposedly balanced psychiatrist.'

———

'The artist, like the God of creation, remains within or behind or beyond or above his handiwork, invisible, refined out of existence, indifferent, paring his fingernails.'

JAMES JOYCE, *A Portrait of the Artist as a Young Man*

October 27th

1930 – Virginia Woolf remarked: 'How comfortless & uneasy my room is – a table all choked with papers &c. I'm now grinding out Waves again ... '

———

My book, stuffed with phrases, has dropped to the floor. It lies under the table, to be swept up by the charwoman when she comes wearily at dawn looking for scraps of paper, old tram tickets, and here and there a note screwed into a ball and left with the litter to be swept up. What is the phrase for the moon? And the phrase for love? By what name are we to call death?

The Waves

October 28th

1910 – Having renounced his ancestral claim to his estates and all his worldly goods, Leo Tolstoy left his family intent on starting a new life. He only made it to the Astapovo train station where he died in the station-master's home on 20 November. He was eighty-two.

'My reason will still not understand why I pray, but I shall still pray, and my life, my whole life, independently of anything that may happen to me, is every moment of it no longer meaningless as it was before, but has an unquestionable meaning of goodness with which I have the power to invest it.'

Anna Karenina

October 29th

1924 – Frances Hodgson Burnett, having spent much of her life in America, died in New York at the age of seventy-four.

Illustration from *A Little Princess*

'What are you laughing at, you bold, impudent child?' Miss Minchin exclaimed.

It took Sara a few seconds to control herself sufficiently to remember that she was a princess. Her cheeks were red and smarting from the blows she had received.

'I was thinking,' she answered.

'Beg my pardon immediately,' said Miss Minchin.

Sara hesitated a second before she replied.

'I will beg your pardon for laughing, if it was rude,' she said then, 'but I won't beg your pardon for thinking.'

A Little Princess

October 30th

1953 – Somerset Maugham reported that the pain in his right hand was caused by 'wastage of the muscle due to wear and tear'. His body was 'rebelling against the demands of his profession'.

———

'I was so pleased to see Willie again, that old, old parrot, with his flat black eyes, blinking and attentive, his courtly politeness and hypnotic stammer ... an old Gladstone bag covered with labels. God only knows what is inside.'

CHRISTOPHER ISHERWOOD

October 31st

1935 – Sibyl, Marchioness of Queensberry, died aged ninety-one, and was buried at the Franciscan Monastery in Sussex. When her son, Lord Alfred Douglas, died on 20 March 1945, he joined her and a single gravestone covers them both.

I know that when plays last too long spectators tire. My tragedy has lasted far too long; its climax is over; its end is mean; and I am quite conscious of the fact that when the end does come I shall return as an unwelcome visitant to a world that does not want me.

OSCAR WILDE

Illustration from *Cider with Rosie*

November 1st

1891 – Stephen Crane was born in Newark, New Jersey. He began writing at the age of four, and in his short life became a celebrated literary figure on both sides of the Atlantic, notably for his undoubted masterpiece about the American Civil War.

It was a ghastly battle. Over his face was the bleach of death, but set upon it were the dark and hard lines of desperate purpose. With this terrible grin of resolution he hugged his precious flag to him and was stumbling and staggering in his design to go the way that led to safety for it.

The Red Badge of Courage

November 2nd

1960 – Penguin Books were found not guilty at the Old Bailey, having been prosecuted for publishing an unexpurgated edition of *Lady Chatterley's Lover*.

What a mystery! What a strange heavy weight of mystery, that could lie soft and heavy in one's hand! The root, root of all that is lovely, the primeval root of all full beauty.

Lady Chatterley's Lover

November 3rd

1910 – Leo Tolstoy began dictating a note to Aylmer Maude, his English biographer, as he lay on his deathbed in the stationmaster's house at Astapovo: 'On my way to the place where I wished to be alone I was taken ill … ' He was too weak to finish it.

When Levin thought about what he was and why he lived, he could find no answer and was driven to despair; but when he left off asking himself those questions he seemed to know what he was and why he lived, for he acted and lived unfalteringly and definitely – recently even more unfalteringly than before.

Anna Karenina

November 4th

1926 – Arnold Bennett arrived 'ten minutes late for dinner at H. G. Wells's and H. G. himself was eleven minutes late. The Shaws were there . . and the Leonard Woolfs.'

Shaw talked practically the whole time, which is the same thing as saying that he talked a damn sight too much. After dinner he and Dorothy and Virginia Woolf and H. G. formed a group and never moved. I formed another group with Charlotte Shaw and Jane

Wells, and never moved either. I really wanted to
have a scrap with Virginia Woolf; but got no chance.

ARNOLD BENNETT

November 5th

1664 – Samuel Pepys attended a performance of
Macbeth for the first time and thought it 'admirably
acted'. He enjoyed it so much he saw it seven more
times over the next four years.

———

She should have died hereafter.
There would have been a time for such a word.
Tomorrow, and tomorrow, and tomorrow,
Creeps in this petty pace from day to day,
To the last syllable of recorded time;
And all our yesterdays have lighted fools
The way to dusty death. Out, out, brief candle!
Life's but a walking shadow, a poor player,
That struts and frets his hour upon the stage,
And then is heard no more. It is a tale
Told by an idiot, full of sound and fury,
Signifying nothing.

WILLIAM SHAKESPEARE, *Macbeth*

November 6th

1941 – Death of Maurice Leblanc, creator of the fictional thief and detective Arsène Lupin, often described as the French Sherlock Holmes.

I gave a start. Pierre Onfrey, the perpetrator of the murder in the Rue Lafontaine at Auteuil! Pierre Onfrey, the man who had cut the throats of Madame Delbois and her two daughters. I bent over him. Yes, that was the face which, in the railway-carriage, had aroused in me the memory of features which I had seen before.

'The Mysterious Railway Passenger' from
Vintage Detective Stories

November 7th

1918 – Siegfried Sassoon visited Thomas Hardy and they walked together in a frosty countryside. Sassoon said Hardy was 'the nearest thing to Shakespeare' he would 'ever go for a walk with'.

That night your great guns, unawares,
Shook all our coffins as we lay,
And broke the chancel window-squares.
We thought it was the Judgment-day

And sat upright. While drearisome
Arose the howl of wakened hounds:
The mouse let fall the altar-crumb,
The worms drew back into the mounds ...

THOMAS HARDY, 'Channel Firing' from the
Poetry of the First World War

November 8th

1847 – Bram Stoker was born on the north side of Dublin. He was bedridden with an unknown illness until the age of seven when he made a complete recovery.

For a few seconds she lay in her helpless attitude and disarray. Her face was ghastly, with a pallor which was accentuated by the blood which smeared her lips and cheeks and chin; from her throat trickled a thin stream of blood. Her eyes were mad with terror. Then she put before her face her poor crushed hands, which bore on their whiteness the red mark of the count's terrible grip, and from behind them came a low desolate wail which made the terrible scream seem only the quick expression of an endless grief.

Dracula

November 9th

1867 – Charles Dickens sailed to America for his second tour. His schedule was so punishing that by the time of his return in April 1868 he could hardly manage solid food and was subsisting on champagne and eggs beaten in sherry.

Illustration from *Great Expectations*

For a day or two, I lay on the sofa, or on the floor – anywhere, according as I happened to sink down – with a heavy head and aching limbs, and no purpose, and no power. Then there came one night which appeared of great duration, and which teemed with anxiety and horror; and when in the morning I tried to sit up in my bed ... I found I could not do so.

Great Expectations

November 10th

1989 – In Richard Eyre's production at the National Theatre, Ian Charleston delivered 'the definitive performance of Hamlet'.

———

But that I am forbid
To tell the secrets of my prison-house,
I could a tale unfold whose lightest word
Would harrow up thy soul, freeze thy young blood,
Make thy two eyes like stars start from their spheres ...
And each particular hair to stand on end ...

WILLIAM SHAKESPEARE, *Hamlet*

November 11th

1985 – Robert Graves was one of sixteen Great War poets commemorated on a stone unveiled in Poets' Corner; he was the only one still alive. He died a few months later.

———

The bugler sent a call of high romance –
'Lights out! Lights out!' to the deserted square.
On the thin brazen notes he threw a prayer,
'God, if it's this for me next time in France ...
Oh spare the phantom bugle as I lie
Dead in the gas and smoke and roar of guns,
Dead in a row with the other broken ones
Lying so stiff and still under the sky,
Jolly young Fusiliers too good to die.'

ROBERT GRAVES, 'The Last Post' from
Poetry of the First World War

———

November 12th

1865 – Elizabeth Gaskell died suddenly, but peacefully, while taking tea in the afternoon.

———

I can testify to a magnificent family red silk umbrella, under which a gentle little spinster, left alone of many brothers and sisters, used to patter to church on rainy days. Have you any red silk umbrellas in London? We had a tradition of the first that had ever been seen in Cranford; and the little boys mobbed it, and called it 'a stick in petticoats'. It might have been the very red silk one I have described, held up by a strong father over a troop of little ones; the poor little lady – the survivor of all – could scarcely carry it.

Cranford

November 13th

1850 – Robert Louis Stevenson was born in Edinburgh. His father was a lighthouse engineer – lighthouse design was the family profession.

Mr Robert Stevenson, that delightful master of delicate and faithful prose. There is such a thing as robbing a story of its reality by trying to make it too true, and *The Black Arrow* is so inartistic as not to contain a single anachronism to boast of, while the transformation of Dr Jekyll reads like an experiment out of the *Lancet*.

OSCAR WILDE

November 14th

1918 – The eve of T. S. Eliot's first visit to the Hogarth Press to be introduced to Virginia and Leonard Woolf. Virginia found him 'a polished, cultivated, elaborate young American, talking so slow that each word seems to have special finish allotted it. But beneath the surface ... he is very intellectual, intolerant, with strong views of his own, & a poetic creed.

> Words strain,
> Crack and sometimes break, under the burden,
> Under the tension, slip, slide, perish,
> Decay with imprecision, will not stay in place,
> Will not stay still.

T. S. ELIOT, *Four Quartets*

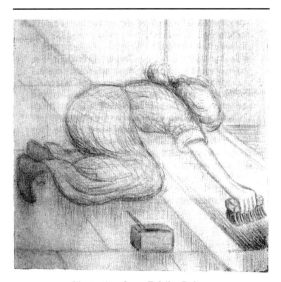

Illustration from *Zuleika Dobson*

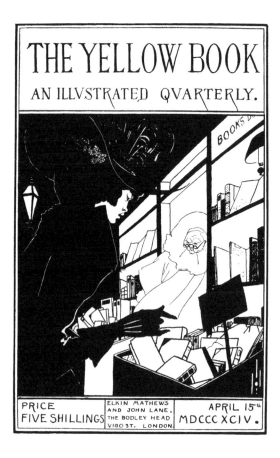

THE YELLOW BOOK

AN ILLVSTRATED QVARTERLY.

BOOKS

PRICE
FIVE SHILLINGS

ELKIN MATHEWS
AND JOHN LANE,
THE BODLEY HEAD
VIGO ST. LONDON.

APRIL 15th
MDCCC XCIV.

November 15th

1869 – Charlotte Mew was born in Bloomsbury. Of her many siblings three died in early childhood and two were committed to mental institutions. Charlotte and her surviving sister vowed never to marry for fear of passing insanity on to their children. Thomas Hardy called her 'far and away the best living woman poet'. She also wrote prose and her short story 'Passed' appeared in *The Yellow Book* in 1894.

A timidly protesting fragrance stole strangely by ... It summoned a stinging memory. I stepped forward to escape it, but stopped, confronted by the being who had shared, by the flickering lamplight and in the presence of that silent witness, the poor little violet's prayer.

from 'Passed'

November 16th

1835 – Halley's Comet's closest ever approach to earth. Samuel Langhorne Clemens (Mark Twain) was born on 30 November of that year. He surmised: 'The Almighty has said, "Now here are these two unaccountable freaks: they came in together, they must go out together." ' He died 21 April 1910, one day after the comet's closest approach that year.

There was a rustle in the gallery which nobody noticed; a moment later the church door creaked; the minister raised his streaming eyes above his handkerchief, and stood transfixed! First one and then another pair of eyes followed the minister's and then, almost with one impulse, the congregation rose and stared while the three dead boys came marching up the aisle, Tom in the lead, Joe next, and Huck, a ruin of drooping rags, sneaking sheepishly in the rear. They had been hid in the unused gallery, listening to their own funeral sermon!

The Adventures of Tom Sawyer

November 17th

1851 – Herman Melville ended a letter to Nathaniel Hawthorne: 'P.P.S. Don't think that by writing me a letter, you shall always be bored with an immediate reply to it – and so keep both of us delving over a writing-desk eternally. No such thing! I shan't always answer your letters, and you may do just as you please.'

———

Genius, all over the world, stands hand in hand, and one shock of recognition runs the whole circle round.

HERMAN MELVILLE, *Hawthorne and His Mosses*

November 18th

1871 – R. F. Benson was born at Wellington College where his father was headmaster (before becoming Archbishop of Canterbury). R. F. was ordained by his father in 1895. Like his brothers, E. F. and A. C., he was a prolific writer of ghost stories.

———

'Well, I mustn't keep you, but I've been thinking while you've been in church of an old story that is told by antiquarians about this place. They say that one of St Thomas à Becket's murderers came here on the very evening of the murder. It is his day today, you know, and that is what put me in mind of it, I suppose.'

'The Traveller' from *Spinechillers*

Illustration from *Zuleika Dobson*

November 19th

1918 – In a letter to her sister, Virginia Woolf reported that Ottoline Morrell found Siegfried Sassoon 'terribly, terribly *spoilt*. I *never* want to see him again. So coarse, so ordinary, so just like any other conceited young guardsman. I felt he had been seeing *odious* people who had changed him *completely*.'

You love us when we're heroes, home on leave,
Or wounded in a mentionable place.
You worship decorations; you believe
That chivalry redeems the war's disgrace.
You make us shells. You listen with delight,
By tales of dirt and danger fondly thrilled.
You crown our distant ardours while we fight,
And mourn our laurelled memories when we're killed.
You can't believe that British troops 'retire'
When hell's last horror breaks them, and they run,
Trampling the terrible corpses – blind with blood.
    O German mother dreaming by the fire,
    While you are knitting socks to send your son
    His face is trodden deeper in the mud.

SIEGFRIED SASSOON, 'Glory of Women' from
Poetry of the First World War

November 20th

1922 – Erskine Childers was sentenced to death by a military court for possessing arms and was executed by firing squad four days later. His last words were, 'Come closer, boys. It will be easier for you.'

I was awakened at ten o'clock on the 19th, after a long and delicious sleep, by Davies's voice outside, talking his unmistakable German. Looking out, in my pyjamas, I saw him on the quay above in conversation with a man in a long mackintosh coat and a gold-laced navy cap. He had a close-trimmed auburn beard, a keen, handsome face, and an animated manner. It was raining in a raw air.

The Riddle of the Sands

Illustration from *Three Men in a Boat*

November 21st

1940 – Ernest Hemingway married his third wife, Martha Gelhorn. Scott Fitzgerald observed: 'It will be odd to think of Ernest married to a really attractive woman. I think the pattern will be somewhat different than with his Pygmalion-like creations.'

Daisy was my second cousin once removed, and I'd known Tom in college ... I had no sight into Daisy's heart, but I felt that Tom would drift on for ever, seeking, a little wistfully, for the dramatic turbulence of some irrecoverable football game.

SCOTT FITZGERALD, *The Great Gatsby*

November 22nd

1916 – Having been very ill and in great pain, Jack London died of uremia aggravated by an accidental (or deliberate?) overdose of morphine.

Because men, groping in the Arctic darkness, had found a yellow metal ... thousands of men were rushing into the Northland. These men wanted dogs, and the dogs they wanted were heavy dogs, with strong muscles by which to toil, and furry coats to protect them from the frost.

The Call of the Wild

_____

_____

_____

Illustration from *The Best of Sherlock Holmes*

November 23rd

1902 – James Joyce told Lady Gregory, promoter of the Irish Revival: 'I want to achieve myself – little or great as I may be ... Accordingly, I am leaving this country and am going to Paris.'

———

Welcome, O life! I go to encounter for the millionth time the reality of experience and to forge in the smithy of my soul the uncreated conscience of my race ... Old father, old artificer, stand me now and ever in good stead.

A Portrait of the Artist as a Young Man

November 24th

1849 – Frances Hodgson Burnett was born into a comfortable middle-class family destined to fall on hard times when her father died of a stroke four years later.

———

When Mary Lennox was sent to Misselthwaite Manor to live with her uncle everybody said she was the most disagreeable-looking child ever seen. It was true, too. She had a little thin face and a little thin body, thin light hair and a sour expression. Her hair was yellow, and her face was yellow because she had been born in India and had always been ill in one way or another.

The Secret Garden

November 25th

1890 – Birth of Isaac Rosenberg into an East End Jewish family of Russian descent. A gifted artist who studied at the Slade and an outstanding war poet, he was killed on the Western Front in 1918.

Sombre the night is.
And though we have our lives, we know
What sinister threat lurks there ...

'Returning, We Hear the Larks' from
Poetry of the First World War

November 26th

1902 – W. B. Yeats invited James Joyce to breakfast with him on his way through London to Paris.

Ah, Exiles wandering over lands and seas,
And planning, plotting always that some morrow
May set a stone upon ancestral Sorrow!
I also bear a bell-branch full of ease.

'The Dedication to a Book of Stories
selected from the Irish Novelists' from
Collected Poems of W. B. Yeats

November 27th

1913 – D. H. Lawrence wrote to John Middleton Murry: 'A woman unsatisfied must have luxuries. But a woman who loves a man would sleep on a board.'

———

She bent forward, trying to see and to understand. Her free, fine curls tickled his face. He started as if they had been red hot, shuddering. He saw her peering forward at the page, her red lips parted piteously, the black hair springing in fine strands across her tawny, ruddy cheek. She was coloured like a pomegranate for richness. His breath came short as he watched her. Suddenly she looked up at him. Her dark eyes were naked with their love, afraid, and yearning.

Sons and Lovers

———

November 28th

1919 – Virginia Woolf found Katherine Mansfield's review of *Night and Day* irritating – 'I thought I saw spite in it.'

———

The dinner party last night went off: the delicate things were discussed. We could both wish that one's first impression of K. M. was not that she stinks like a – well, civet cat that had taken to street walking. [K. M. was very fond of French perfume.]

VIRGINIA WOOLF

November 29th

1832 – Louisa May Alcott was born in Philadelphia. Famed for her portrayal of idyllic, nineteenth-century American family life with its triumphs and tragedies, she was in her youth much influenced by her father's friends Emerson and Thoreau, to the latter of whom she formed a strongly romantic attachment.

As young readers like to know 'how people look', we will take this moment to give them a little sketch of the four sisters, who sat knitting away in the twilight. It was a comfortable old room, though the carpet was faded and the furniture very plain; for a good picture or two hung on the walls, books filled the recesses, chrysanthemums and Christmas roses bloomed in the windows, and a pleasant atmosphere of home-peace pervaded it ...

Little Women & Good Wives

November 30th

1900 – Oscar Wilde died of cerebral meningitis on a wintry night in Paris with his friend Robbie Ross and a Catholic priest at his bedside.

When they entered they found, hanging upon the wall, a splendid portrait of their master as they had last seen him, in all the wonder of his exquisite youth and beauty. Lying on the floor was a dead man, in evening dress, with a knife in his heart. He was withered, wrinkled, and loathsome of visage. It was not till they had examined the rings that they recognised who it was.

The Picture of Dorian Gray

Illustrations from *Zuleika Dobson*

December 1st

1896 – Jeffery Day was born in Huntingdonshire. In 1914 he joined the Royal Naval Air Service. In February 1918 he was shot down by six German aircraft which he attacked single-handedly out to sea. With his machine in flames he landed perfectly on the water but waved his fellow pilots back to base because he knew there was no way they could help him.

The air is clear, more clear than sparkling wine;
Compared with this wine is a turgid brew.
The far horizon makes a clean-cut line
Between the silver and depthless blue.
Out of the snow-white level reared on high
Glittering hills surge up to meet the sky.

'On the Wings of the Morning' from
Poetry of the First World War

December 2nd

1925 – At Oxford, after a meeting of the Essay Club, A. L. Rowse met Robert Graves and found him 'a queer, charming fellow . . His craze for analysing motives and psychological phenomena must be due to that slight unbalance left over from the war.'

I was thinking, too, what opportunities I should have, as Emperor, for consulting the secret archives and finding out just what happened on this occasion or on that. How many twisted stories still remained to be straightened out! What a miraculous fate for an historian! And as you will have seen, I took full advantage of my opportunities. Even the mature historian's privilege of setting forth conversations of which he knows only the gist is one that I have availed myself of hardly at all.

I, Claudius

December 3rd

1894 – Robert Louis Stevenson was talking to his wife and straining to open a bottle of wine when he collapsed and died of a brain haemorrhage in Samoa aged forty-four.

———

My eyes fell upon my hand ... It was the hand of Edward Hyde.

I must have stared upon it for near half a minute, sunk as I was in the mere stupidity of wonder, before terror woke up in my breast as sudden and startling as the crash of cymbals; and bounding from my bed, I rushed to the mirror. At the sight that met my eyes, my blood was changed into something exquisitely thin and icy. Yes, I had gone to bed Henry Jekyll, I had awakened Edward Hyde.

The Strange Case of Dr Jekyll and Mr Hyde
and Other Stories

December 4th

1949 – Raymond Chandler wrote: 'Of course Maugham is right, as he always is. It is much more difficult to write plays, harder work ... It is all clear and literal and immediate. The novelist, if he is any good, gives you a thousand things that he never actually says.'

———

Then there was Somerset Maugham, a grim figure; rat-eyed; dead-man cheeked, unshaven; a criminal I should have said had I met him in a bus.

VIRGINIA WOOLF

December 5th

1870 – Alexandre Dumas père died at his son's villa near Dieppe. He was buried in a local cemetery but his remains were moved to the Pantheon in Paris in 2002.

This strange pile, this prison whose very name spelt terror, this fortress around which Marseilles had woven its legends for the past three hundred years, rising up so suddenly before Dantès, had the effect on him that the sight of a scaffold must have on a condemned man.

The Count of Monte Cristo

December 6th

1882 – Anthony Trollope died in London. He is buried in Kensal Green Cemetery, near his contemporary Wilkie Collins and not far from Thackeray.

There was no loud rattle in the throat, no dreadful struggle, no palpable sign of death; but the lower jaw fell a little from its place, and the eyes, which had been so constantly closed in sleep, now remained fixed and open. Neither Mr Harding nor Dr Grantly knew that life was gone, though both suspected it.

Barchester Towers

December 7th

1985 – Robert Graves died in his adopted Mallorcan village of Deyá at the age of ninety.

Yet I do not seem to have changed much, mentally or physically, since I came to live here, though I can no longer read a newspaper without glasses, or run upstairs three steps at a time, and have to watch my weight. And if condemned to relive those lost years I should probably behave again in very much the same way; a conditioning in the Protestant morality of the English governing classes, though qualified by mixed blood, a rebellious nature and an overriding poetic obsession, is not easily outgrown.

Goodbye to All That

December 8th

1835 – Branwell Brontë tirelessly but fruitlessly tried to interest the editor of *Blackwood's Magazine* in his talents as a contributor: 'You have lost an able writer in James Hogg and God grant you may gain one in Patrick Branwell Brontë.'

Sir – I most earnestly entreat you to read and pass your judgement upon what I have sent you, because from the day of my birth to this nineteenth [actually twentieth] year of my life I have lived among secluded hills, where I could neither know what I was or what I could do. I read for the same reason that I ate or drank; because it was a real craving of nature. I wrote on the same principle as I spoke – out of the impulse and feelings of the mind; nor could I help it, for what came, came out, and there was the end of it. For as to self-conceit, that could not receive food from flattery, since to this hour not half a dozen people in the world know I have penned a line ...

BRANWELL BRONTË to William Wordsworth

December 9th

1847 – Birth of a somebody – George Grossmith – in Islington.

————

AUGUST 16 – Lupin positively refused to walk down the Parade with me because I was wearing my new straw helmet with my frock-coat. I don't know what the boy is coming to.

The Diary of a Nobody

December 10th

1914 – Virginia Woolf managed to cook her wedding ring into a suet pudding.

———

Dalloway was falling in love with her; she was falling in love with Dalloway ... He said to himself as they were getting into the boat, 'She will marry that man,' dully, without any resentment; but it was an obvious thing. Dalloway would marry Clarissa.

Mrs Dalloway

December 11th

1921 – Virginia Woolf wrote in her diary: ' ... for perhaps the 50th time, I am frustrated as I mean to write to poor T. Hardy. I pray that he sits safe & sound by his fireside at this moment. May all bicycles, bronchitis & influenza keep far from him.'

———

The man was of fine figure, swarthy, and stern in aspect; and he showed in profile a facial angle so slightly inclined as to be almost perpendicular. He wore a short jacket of brown corduroy, newer than the remainder of his suit, which was a fustian waist-coat with white horn buttons, breeches of the same, tanned leggings, and a straw hat overlaid with black glazed canvas ... His measured, springless walk was the walk of the skilled countryman as distinct from the desultory shamble of the general labourer; while in the turn and plant of each foot there was, further, a dogged and cynical indifference personal to himself, showing its presence even in the regularly inter-changing fustian folds, now in the left leg, now in the right, as he paced along.

The Mayor of Casterbridge

December 12th

1821 – Gustave Flaubert was born in Rouen. His first novel, *Madame Bovary*, caused moral outrage.

Besides, she was growing very sentimental. She had insisted on exchanging miniatures; they had cut off handfuls of hair, and now she was asking for a ring – a real wedding-ring, in sign of an eternal union ... He had possessed so few women of such ingenuousness. This love without debauchery was a new experience for him, and, drawing him out of his lazy habits, caressed at once his pride and his sensuality. Emma's enthusiasm, which his bourgeois good sense disdained, seemed to him in his heart of hearts charming, since it was lavished on him. Then, sure of being loved, he no longer kept up appearances, and insensibly his ways changed.

Madame Bovary

December 13th

1972 – Death of L. P. Hartley, widely remembered for the opening sentence of *The Go-Between*: 'The past is a foreign country; they do things differently there.'

Her face was wet with tears.

A foreigner in the world of the emotions, ignorant of their language but compelled to listen to it ... I turned in at the lodge gates, wondering how I should say what I had come to say, when the south-west prospect of the Hall, long hidden from my memory, sprang into view.

The Go-Between

Illustration from
Ballet Shoes

December 14th

1941 – Death of Jessie Pope, passionately patriotic poet, writer and journalist, remembered for her motivational poems during World War I.

Who'll earn the Empire's thanks –
Will you, my laddie?
Who'll swell the victor's ranks –
Will you, my laddie?
When that procession comes,
Banners and rolling drums –
Who'll stand and bite his thumbs –
Will you, my laddie?

'The Call' from *Poetry of the First World War*

December 15th

1929 – The Woolfs went to Wyndham's Theatre to see *The Calendar* by Edgar Wallace. King George V was there and Queen Mary 'like a lit-up street with diamonds'.

To be successful in robbery one must be something of a psychologist. It is not sufficient to know where material danger is to be found: one must be able to read the mind of one's opponent.

EDGAR WALLACE, 'The Mind-Reader'
from *Vintage Detective Stories*

December 16th

1775 – Jane Austen was born, into a close-knit family located on the lower fringes of the English landed gentry.

Whatever 'Bloomsbury' may think of Jane Austen, she is not by any means one of my favourites. I'd give all she ever wrote for half what the Brontës wrote – if my reason did not compel me to see that she is a magnificent artist. What I shall proceed to find out, from her letters, when I've time, is why she failed to be much better than she was. Something to do with sex, I expect; the letters are full of hints already that she suppressed half of her in her novels.

VIRGINIA WOOLF

December 17th

1873 – Ford Madox Ford was born Ford Herman Hueffer. On his fortieth birthday in 1913 he sat down to write the novel he called his 'best book', *The Good Soldier*. Graham Greene was a great admirer. He said: 'No one in our century except James has been more attentive to the craft of letters.' Rebecca West said that being embraced by him was like being 'the toast under a poached egg'. But she was also an admirer of his work and influence and praised *The Good Soldier* as 'a much better book than any of us deserves'.

———

It appeared to her that it was Leonora's business to save her husband's body; she, Nancy, possessed his soul – a precious thing that she would shield and bear away up in her arms – as if Leonora were a hungry dog, trying to spring up at a lamb that she was carrying. Yes, she felt as if Edward's love were a precious lamb that she were bearing away from a cruel and predatory beast. For, at that time, Leonora appeared to her as a cruel and predatory beast. Leonora, Leonora with her hunger, with her cruelty, had driven Edward to madness.

The Good Soldier

Illustration from *Three Men in a Boat*

December 18th

1870 – H. H. Munro, better known by his pen name Saki, was born in Burma.

From the farthest window of the dining-room the door of the shed could just be seen ... He saw the Woman enter, and then he imagined her opening the door of the sacred hutch and peering down with her short-sighted eyes into the thick straw bed where his god lay hidden. Perhaps she would prod at the straw in her clumsy impatience. And Conradin fervently breathed his prayer for the last time ... The loud foolish screaming of the maid, the answering chorus of wondering ejaculations from the kitchen region, the scuttering footsteps and hurried embassies for outside help, and then, after a lull, the scared sobbings and the shuffling tread of those who bore a heavy burden into the house.

'Sredni Vashtar' from *Saki: The Best Short Stories*

Illustration from
The Jungle Book

December 19th

1848 – Emily Brontë died of tuberculosis at the age of thirty, barely three months after her brother Branwell's funeral.

———

I heard distinctly the gusty wind, and the driving of the snow; I heard, also, the fir bough repeat its teasing sound, and ascribed it to the right cause: but it annoyed me so much, that I resolved to silence it, if possible; and, I thought, I rose and endeavoured to unhasp the casement. The hook was soldered into the staple: a circumstance observed by me when awake, but forgotten. 'I must stop it, nevertheless!' I muttered, knocking my knuckles through the glass, and stretching an arm out to seize the importunate branch; instead of which, my fingers closed on the fingers of a little, ice-cold hand! The intense horror of nightmare came over me: I tried to draw back my arm, but the hand clung to it, and a most melancholy voice sobbed, 'Let me in – let me in!' ... Terror made me cruel; and, finding it useless to attempt shaking the creature off, I pulled its wrist on to the broken pane, and rubbed it to and fro till the blood ran down and soaked the bedclothes ...

Wuthering Heights

December 20th

1965 – Somerset Maugham was cremated in Marseilles, with only Alan Searle present.

He was the most sexually voracious man I've ever known. BEVERLEY NICHOLS

December 21st

1940 – Scott Fitzgerald died of a heart attack at Sheila Grahame's apartment in Hollywood.

Outwardly they showed no signs of deterioration. Gloria at twenty-six was still the Gloria of twenty; her complexion a fresh damp setting for her candid eyes; her hair still a childish glory, darkening slowly from corn colour to a deep russet gold; her slender body suggesting ever a nymph running and dancing through Orphic groves ... And for his part Anthony had rather gained than lost in appearance; his face had taken on a certain intangible air of tragedy, romantically contrasted with his trim and immaculate person.

The Beautiful and Damned

December 22nd

1880 – Two years after the death of George Lewis, the man to whom she had been married in everything but name, George Eliot married John Cross, who had been a comfort to her in her bereavement. She herself died, however, only months later, at their new house in Chelsea.

Gold! – his own gold – brought back to him as mysteriously as it had been taken away! He felt his heart begin to beat violently, and for a few moments he was unable to stretch out his hand and grasp the restored treasure. The heap of gold seemed to glow and get larger beneath his agitated gaze. He leaned forward at last, and stretched forth his hand; but instead of the hard coin with the familiar resisting outline, his fingers encountered soft warm curls.

Silas Marner

December 23rd

1863 – William Makepeace Thackeray, who had an addiction to spicy peppers, suffered a stroke after dining out and died in the night. Seven thousand people attended his funeral.

No more firing was heard at Brussels – the pursuit rolled miles away. Darkness came down on the field and city; and Amelia was praying for George, who was lying on his face, dead, with a bullet through his heart.

Vanity Fair

December 24th

1895 – Noel Streatfeild was born in Sussex, the second of the five children of William Streatfeild, later Bishop of Lewis. She was the 'plain' sister.

Gum, to whom time meant very little indeed, was never able to remember that other people might not be expecting him when he turned up without a word of warning after being away for months. This time he opened his front door, put down his hold-all, and looked round for a suitable place to put the baby. Seeing nowhere but the hall table or the umbrella stand, he called rather angrily for Sylvia.

Ballet Shoes

December 25th

1959 – Graham Greene wrote that he went to the home of his mother's cousin, Robert Louis Stevenson, in Samoa: 'Yesterday in pouring rain I visited Valima.' It was too muddy to reach the grave, but 'very beautiful & a famous waterfall'.

———

The doctor's phrase – an innocent – came back to me; and I was wondering if that were, after all, the true description, when the road began to go down into the narrow and naked chasm of a torrent. The waters thundered tumultuously in the bottom; and the ravine was filled full of the sound, the thin spray and the claps of wind that accompanied their descent. The scene was certainly impressive; but the road was in that part very securely walled in; the mule went steadily forward; and I was astonished to perceive the paleness of terror in the face of my companion.

R. L. STEVENSON, 'Olalla' from *The Strange Case of Dr Jekyll and Mr Hyde and Other Stories*

December 26th

1913 – Ambrose Bierce, having travelled to Mexico to gain first-hand experience of the Mexican Revolution, disappeared without a trace on this day and was presumed dead.

———

He saw me – at last, at last, he saw me! In the consciousness of that, my terror fled as a cruel dream ... Mad with exultation I shouted – I *must* have shouted – 'He sees, he sees: he will understand!' Then, controlling myself, I moved forward, smiling and consciously beautiful, to offer myself to his arms, to comfort him with endearments, and, with my son's hand in mine, to speak words that should restore the broken bonds between the living and the dead.

Alas! alas! his face went white with fear, his eyes were as those of a hunted animal. He backed away from me as I advanced, and at last turned and fled ...

'The Moonlit Road' from *Spinechillers*

December 27th

1940 – Scott Fitzgeralds's funeral took place in Rockville, Maryland. At the time of his death it was incorrectly reported that his books were out of print. The truth was even sadder. All nine of his books were in stock but in 1940 they sold a total of seventy-two copies.

If you should look through the files of old magazines for the first years of the present century you would find, sandwiched in between the stories of Richard Harding Davis and Frank Norris and others long since dead, the work of one Jeffrey Curtain: a novel or

284

two, and perhaps three or four dozen short stories. You could, if you were interested, follow them along until, say, 1908, when they suddenly disappeared.

'The Lees of Happiness' in *Tales of the Jazz Age*

December 28th

1949 – On being given a copy of *The Thirty-Nine Steps*, Raymond Chandler wrote: 'I liked the dedication in which Buchan said "the romance where the incidents defy the probabilities, and march just inside the borders of the possible". That's a pretty good formula for the thriller of any kind.'

I had a cigar in my mouth, I remember, as I pushed open the smoking-room door. The lights were not lit, which struck me as odd. I wondered if Scudder had turned in already.

I snapped the switch, but there was nobody there. Then I saw something in the far corner which made me drop my cigar and fall into a cold sweat.

My guest was lying sprawled on his back. There was a long knife through his heart which skewered him to the floor.

The Thirty-Nine Steps

December 29th

1899 – Stephen Crane suffered a severe haemorrhage of the lungs at Brede Place, his English home in Sussex; he died at a health spa in Germany on 5 June 1900 at the age of twenty-eight.

―――――

When the roof fell in, a great funnel of smoke swarmed towards the sky, as if the old man's mighty spirit, released from its body – a little bottle – had swelled like the genie of fable. The smoke was tinted rose-hue from the flames, and perhaps the unutterable midnights of

the universe will have no power to daunt the colour of this soul.

'The Veteran' from *The Red Badge of Courage and Other Stories*

December 30th

1895 – L(eslie) P(oles) Hartley was born near Cambridge. Although named Leslie after Virginia Woolf's father, he was seen as 'a dull fat man' and rebuffed by the Bloomsbury Group.

———

[The diary] began to recover its value for me, I felt its power returning. How wonderful if I could make it the instrument of my vengeance! There would be poetic justice in that. Moreover my enemies would be off their guard, they would never suspect danger from a gun they had so thoroughly spiked. And at the same time their consciences would not be quite easy about it, it would be a symbol of the injury they had done me, and they would be all the more sensitive to an attack from it.

The Go-Between

December 31st

1927 – Max Beerbohm wrote to Virginia Woolf: 'Your novels beat me – black and blue.'

In those days it was the fashion for young ladies to embroider slippers for such men in holy orders as best pleased their fancy. I received hundreds – thousands – of such slippers ... I had hoarded them with a fatuous pride. On the evening of my betrothal I made a bonfire of them, visible from three counties. I danced round it all night.' And from his old eyes darted even now the reflections of those flames.

Zuleika Dobson